Moonology
Diary 2019

Yasmin Boland

HAY HOUSE
Carlsbad, California • New York City
London • Sydney • New Delhi

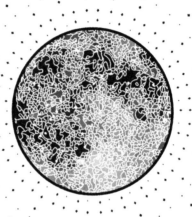

This diary belongs to

....

Published in the United Kingdom by:
Hay House UK Ltd, Astley House, 33 Notting Hill Gate,
London W11 3JQ
Tel: +44 (0)20 3675 2450; Fax: +44 (0)20 3675 2451;
www.hayhouse.co.uk

Published in Australia by:
Hay House Australia Ltd, 18/36 Ralph St, Alexandria NSW 2015
Tel: (61) 2 9669 4299; Fax: (61) 2 9669 4144
www.hayhouse.com.au

Published in India by:
Hay House Publishers India, Muskaan Complex, Plot No.3, B-2,
Vasant Kunj, New Delhi 110 070
Tel: (91) 11 4176 1620; Fax: (91) 11 4176 1630
www.hayhouse.co.in

A catalogue record for this book is available from the British Library.

ISBN: 978-1-78817-022-2

Interior images: 19 Nyx Rowan; all other illustrations WumiStudio/
Creative Market

Printed and bound by CPI Group (UK) Ltd, Croydon CR0 4YY

Contents

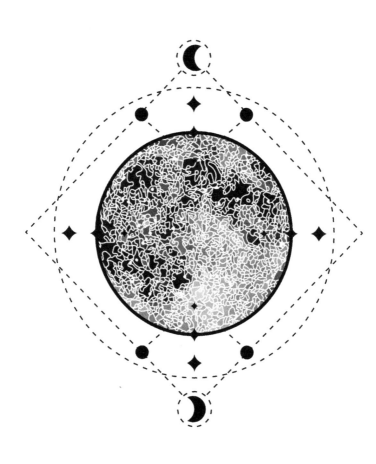

Working with the Magic of Lunar Cycles

Welcome to the *Moonology Diary 2019*! What you're about to learn and do could change your life for the better, forever.

This diary is all about learning how to work with the cycles of the Moon to create, plan and predict your life. Living in alignment with the Moon – as you'll find – is one of the most powerful things you can do for yourself.

Working with the Moon can help you to create whatever life you're dreaming of. It can also help you to live an energetically clear life, it can turn you into a powerful manifestor, and it can reduce your stress, up your vitality and give you a cosmic timer for your life.

Why wouldn't you do it?

The most wonderful thing about making promises at the start of this new year is that I know this diary can truly help me, and you, to fulfil them. All we need to do is show up! That means working with the diary every week.

I have worked with thousands of people over the years and seen the power of working with the Moon in action.

It's natural, it's feminine and it's more powerful than you can imagine.

A lunar cycle is the time is takes for the Moon to pass through its eight main phases (New, Crescent, First Quarter, Gibbous, Full, Disseminating, Third Quarter and Balsamic), and this takes just less than 30 days. In this diary, you only need to think about the main four phases, one of which we move through almost every week:

●	**New Moon** – the start of the lunar cycle when the Sun and Moon are at the same place in the zodiac. A time to make wishes and set intentions.
◐	**First Quarter Moon** – about a week after the New Moon and a week before the Full Moon. This is the time to work doubly hard on your dreams.
○	**Full Moon** – emotions come to the surface. This is a time to do energetic work and release all negativity via forgiveness and ritual.
◑	**Third Quarter Moon** – about one week after the Full Moon. It's time to let go, accept, surrender and make peace.

As you begin to fill in the diary pages, you'll notice each of these Moon phases has a very powerful vibration. Once you start to align yourself with these vibrations using written and spoken words, rituals, and connection to the Divine, you'll start to live in alignment with All That Is. It's amazing, and yes, it's magical, so let's get started!

New and Full Moon Energies

I f you're new to Moonology, you may not know that women (and some men) have been doing energetic work in time with the Moon for millennia. The Divine Feminine is rising and taking us all to the Moon with her! The Moon represents the feminine, the Divine Feminine, the mother, the sorceress, the witch, the goddess and all women everywhere. She also represents (astrologically) breasts, mothering, the home and pregnancy, among other things.

Live in tune with the Moon, and you'll come to understand Her rhythms and how much sense they make!

New Moon: Make Wishes and Set Intentions

At the time of the New Moon, new things are beginning and a lot of energy is going into one part of your chart. It's the time to make wishes, set your intentions and also start over in some way, probably in the House (*see p.11*) that the New Moon is triggering. That area of your life is due for a makeover or a restart – it's time to wipe the slate clean.

The Full Moon: Release and Forgive

The Full Moon takes place around two weeks after the New Moon and is a time of heightened emotions, for climaxes and conclusions, and when you receive answers, including to questions posed at the previous New Moon. The Full Moon is also an important time for forgiveness, to practise gratitude and to release negativity. The sign the Full Moon is in can also be used to support any efforts you're making to live consciously and in tune with the Universe.

Full Moon Forgiveness

The way to release upset and break karma between you and someone else is through forgiveness. This is something you can do at any time; however, the end of the year and every Full Moon are super-powerful times for it.

The collective energy for *releasing* is so high at the end of the year, as people all over the Western world prepare to turn a page in their life. They know that one chapter is ending, and another beginning. Even if the end of the year is a man-made demarcation, the combined focus that we all put on it creates a powerful energetic charge.

Then there is the energy at the time of the monthly Full Moon. As you might know the Moon is all about *emotions*, and the Moon is the Queen of Emotions. As the Moon swells, so do our emotions – they come to the surface to be dealt with. The following formula, inspired by the work of Catherine Ponder and taken from my book *Moonology*, can help with both forgiveness and karma release.

Forgiveness Formula

'I forgive everything, everyone, every experience, every
memory of the past or present that needs forgiveness.
I forgive positively everyone. I also forgive myself
of past mistakes. The Universe is love, and I am
forgiven and governed by love alone. Love is now
adjusting my life. Realizing this, I abide in peace.

I bring love and healing to all my thoughts, beliefs and
relationships. I learn my lessons and move on. I call on
my soul fragments to be cleansed by the Full Moon and
I call on them to rejoin me. I send love to myself and
everyone I know, and everyone who knows me, in all
directions of time. Under this glorious Full Moon, I
am healed. My life is healed. And so it is. So be it.'

Make Peace with the Past

My hope is that you had a wonderful 2018. However, if there were issues that you had to deal with, then now is the time to let them go forever. In order to release something, we need to process it. We can't just hope it'll disappear by itself. We need to feel it and make peace with it, and only then can we discharge it from our body, our energetic and emotional bodies and our life, so that we're ready to welcome in the year ahead. So fill in the blanks on the following page.

Releasing the Past

The first thing, person or situation I want to release from my life is:

_____

The lesson I learned from this is:

_____

Even though this happened, I truly and deeply love and approve of myself. The second thing, person or situation I want to release from my life is:

_____

The lesson I learned from this is:

_____

Even though this happened, I truly and deeply love and approve of myself. The third thing, person or situation I want to release from my life is:

_____

The lesson I learned from this is:

_____

Even though this happened, I truly and deeply love and approve of myself.

Creating Magic with the Moon

As I mentioned briefly earlier, you can work with the lunar cycle to create, plan and predict your life. Here's a little more info you'll need to know before you begin your journey with the Moon and Her cycles.

Create Your Life

There's an amazing power in making wishes that come from the heart. Based on the idea that 'If you can believe it, you can conceive it,' it's one of the ways in which we unconsciously create our reality. Look around you: everything you see started as an idea.

Creating, wishing, setting intentions and making commitments at the time of the New Moon is something that we have done for millennia, because energetically it's the right time to do it (literally as soon as possible after the New Moon). Once you begin this monthly process, and back up your wishes with actions, you'll be amazed to see your ability to manifest unfold. There are a few golden rules to observe:

1. Don't meddle with anyone else's free will.

2. Do back up your wishes with action points you can carry out.

3. If at first you don't succeed, wish again (and take action again!)

Plan Your Life

As you work through this diary over the course of the year, you'll see that the New and Full Moons unfold in a regular and predictable order – essentially they work through the signs of the zodiac in the same order as you would read Star signs in a newspaper horoscope: Aries, Taurus, Gemini, Cancer, Leo, Virgo, Libra, Scorpio, Sagittarius, Capricorn, Aquarius and Pisces.

Aries	♈	Libra	♎
Taurus	♉	Scorpio	♏
Gemini	♊	Sagittarius	♐
Cancer	♋	Capricorn	♑
Leo	♌	Aquarius	♒
Virgo	♍	Pisces	♓

Check which astrological sign the New or Full Moon is taking place in, and contemplate what that means before work with Her energies.

Each sign has its own 'flavour', so each New and Full Moon also has its own flavour. There are also certain 'things to do' at New or Full Moon for each astrological sign. Once you know which sign and House (*see p.11*) the New Moon is going to be in, you can start to work with the energies of that sign and make plans accordingly. For example, when it's New Moon in family-friendly Cancer, you can make plans to do with your family; or when the Moon is new in ambitious Capricorn, you can think about planing your professional year ahead, and so on.

Predict Your Life

The Moon can also help you to predict your life. As you have already learned, the New Moon brings new beginnings and the Full Moon brings climaxes and conclusions. If you don't already know your astrological chart, you can have it cast here for free: www.moonmessages.com/freechart.

Once you know where in your chart the New Moon is taking place, not only can you make plans, but you can also make predictions about the issues and opportunities likely to come up for you that month. Similarly with the Full Moon – you can predict in your chart where matters are likely to come to a head.

You don't need to be an astrologer to do this – all will be explained later in the diary. The idea is that if you work with the energies of each lunation during the year ahead, you'll have worked on every part of your life, from your relationships and finances, to health, career and taking time out for yourself.

Manifesting with the New Moon

As well as the release work at the time of the Full Moon, there's also attraction work, manifesting and magic. All of these can be done any day – or night – of the week (we all do it unconsciously 24/7 anyway!), but just after the New Moon is a powerful time to do energetic work. Just as I believe we're here for our souls to evolve, and that astrology and Moonology are tools for that, I also believe we're here to learn about our true power as spiritual beings having a human experience. Note, I'm referring to us humans as spiritual beings just as I call the archangels and goddesses spiritual beings, because we all are!

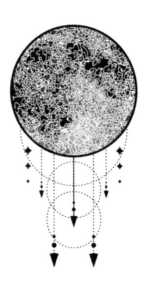

Working with the Houses

One of the reasons we work with the New and Full Moons is to make predictions. Each New and Full Moon triggers a part of your astrological chart called a House, and the simple way to make predictions is to work out which House the New or Full Moon is triggering in your astrological chart. Then refer to the quick guide below to give you an idea of what to expect and focus on in the month ahead.

All you need to know is your Star sign, or better yet your Rising sign as this is calculated using the exact moment of your birth and so will be even more accurate. Then visit www.moonmessages.com/houseschart for a free guide to the Moon in each House and www.moonmessages.com /whyrisingsign for more about Rising signs.

A Quick Guide to the Houses

The 1st House: your appearance and image; self-identity; how you come across to others.

The 2nd House: money, property and possessions; values, including how you value yourself.

The 3rd House: communications; siblings; neighbours; quick trips; early learning and education.

The 4th House: home and family, all things domestic; where you belong; your past.

The 5th House: romance; creativity; kids (your own or someone else's); pursuit of pleasure; love affairs.

The 6th House: daily routines, including at work; your health; duty.

The 7th House: your lovers, your spouse and your ex; open enemies; any sort of partner, including business partners; cooperation and competition.

The 8th House: joint finances; credit cards; debts; sex; anything you consider taboo; inheritance; transformation.

The 9th House: study; travel; the Great Cosmic Quest; the Internet; higher learning; religion; spirituality; dreams.

The 10th House: your career and ambitions; how you make your mark on the world: what you're known for; your reputation.

The 11th House: friends; networks; social circles; hopes and wishes.

The 12th House: your fears; your spirituality; self-undoing; withdrawal; secret or hidden enemies. This is the deepest, darkest, most sensitive part of your chart.

New and Full Moon Rituals

As you'll see as we move through the year, it's always a good time for a ritual!

There are couple of simple basics which are useful to know before you begin:

1. Creating a Sacred Space

Light some white sage, good quality incense and/or Palo Santo wood, play some beautiful spiritual music and open the windows. This will raise the vibration of not just the room but of you too.

2. Building an Altar

Essentially, in your home you want to create a hub which you can use as the focal point for your Moon manifesting and magical work. Think of a small, low table with trinkets and knickknacks, such as candles, sacred Tibetan bells, an incense burner, crystals, beautiful found objects, and pictures of angels, saints and goddesses, such as Jesus, the Hindu goddess Lakshmi, Mother Mary and so on.

Here are a few more ideas for your altar:

- Tarot, goddess cards or angel cards

- A ream of beautiful cloth

- A large or small vase for flowers

- A ghee candle (ghee feeds the angels)

- A photo of someone you love

- A sacred mala or rosary beads

- A small bowl you can burn paper in

Working with the Archangels and Goddesses

In my humble opinion, one of the very best ways to work with the New and Full Moons throughout the year is to use them as a sort of lunar mala. A mala is a beautiful string of beads used for counting as you pray. For example, in India, the number 108 is considered sacred so many malas come with 54 or 108 beads.

I believe that we can use astrology and Moonology in two ways: to create and plan our lives; and to predict our lives. You can do that at every New and Full Moon (and Daily Moon for that matter) too. More on this later.

So, for example, if you want to work with the archangels and goddesses at each New and Full Moon, you can refer to the table opposite for relevant cosmic correspondences. Note there are different beings you can choose to work with at each lunation; they are not set in stone. You can change them around in your own practice without any problem!

Zodiac sign	Archangel/ Ascended Master	God/Goddess
Aries	Ariel	Athena
Taurus	Chamuel	Hathor
Gemini	Zadkiel	Ganesh, Saraswati
Cancer	Gabriel, Saint Germain	Mary, Diana
Leo	Raziel, The Great Mother	Medusa
Virgo	Metatron	Ceres
Libra	Jophiel	Lakshmi, Aphrodite
Scorpio	Jeremiel	Durga, Kali
Sagittarius	Raphael, Raguel	Fortuna
Capricorn	Michael, Azrael	Hera, Juno
Aquarius	Uriel	Isis
Pisces	Sandalphon, Jesus	Kuan Yin

Work with the archangels and goddesses by finding pictures of them online or reading books or posts about them... See how you feel about them and ask the ones you feel a connection to for their help.

☾ A Ritual for New and Full Moon

1. Create a sacred space.

2. Tune in to the goddess or angel of the month.

3. Make an affirmation that suits the sign the New or Full Moon is in, and write it down until you *feel* it.

4. At New Moon, write down your top 10 New Moon wishes or intentions. The secret here is to make sure they come from the heart.

5. At Full Moon, perform your Forgiveness Ceremony.

6. Meditate and contemplate, knowing that the Universe will deliver to you the messages you need to hear.

If you take the time to work with the rhythm of the Moon, one thing is certain – your life will change.

Planning for the Year Ahead

Some people don't like to make New Year's resolutions or set themselves goals. Others have the idea that if they expect little they'll never be disappointed. As you might guess, I'm not one of those people. Maybe it's my Capricorn Moon, but I'm a firm believer in making plans, setting goals and having an overall idea of where you want to go.

Of course, we always need to remain conscious. If something feels wrong as you move towards a goal, or if the energy 'turns', you're probably on the wrong path. Make sure you don't allow your ego to get in your way. Setting goals and making wishes comes with responsibility. If it feels right, it's probably right. If it doesn't, consider taking a new course.

I believe that when you live in accordance with the Moon and start to get clear about what you want, and you start consciously to forgive yourself and others, then you'll start to become a more magical person. And then whatever you manifest should feel pretty perfect. It's how Moonology works. You're using the Moon as a cosmic timer to do your New and Full Moon 'work', and magically increasing your vibration as a part of the process. The higher your vibration, the better. You become more powerful in many good ways. You get to taste the best that life has to offer you in this lifetime, so make the most it!

So I suggest you take some time to write down your goals for 2019. Make your commitments now, and as the New and Full Moons take place during the year. Look at the energies around these wishes, and regularly come back to review them. Each New and Full Moon triggers a different sign or House, so you'll have lots of information to keep you thinking, healing and evolving in every part of your life, as the year unfolds.

I don't believe that spending your year in tune with the Moon should be anything other than a joyous experience, so remember to have fun along the way!

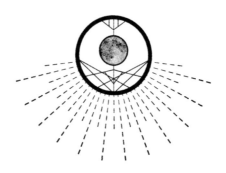

Weekly
Diary

JANUARY

M	T	W	T	F	S	S
	1	2	3	4	5	6
7	8	9	10	11	12	13
14	15	16	17	18	19	20
21	22	23	24	25	26	27
28	29	30	31			

FEBRUARY

M	T	W	T	F	S	S
				1	2	3
4	5	6	7	8	9	10
11	12	13	14	15	16	17
18	19	20	21	22	23	24
25	26	27	28			

MARCH

M	T	W	T	F	S	S
				1	2	3
4	5	6	7	8	9	10
11	12	13	14	15	16	17
18	19	20	21	22	23	24
25	26	27	28	29	30	31

APRIL

M	T	W	T	F	S	S
1	2	3	4	5	6	7
8	9	10	11	12	13	14
15	16	17	18	19	20	21
22	23	24	25	26	27	28
29	30					

MAY

M	T	W	T	F	S	S
		1	2	3	4	5
6	7	8	9	10	11	12
13	14	15	16	17	18	19
20	21	22	23	24	25	26
27	28	29	30	31		

JUNE

M	T	W	T	F	S	S
					1	2
3	4	5	6	7	8	9
10	11	12	13	14	15	16
17	18	19	20	21	22	23
24	25	26	27	28	29	30

JULY

M	T	W	T	F	S	S
1	2	3	4	5	6	7
8	9	10	11	12	13	14
15	16	17	18	19	20	21
22	23	24	25	26	27	28
29	30	31				

AUGUST

M	T	W	T	F	S	S
			1	2	3	4
5	6	7	8	9	10	11
12	13	14	15	16	17	18
19	20	21	22	23	24	25
26	27	28	29	30	31	

SEPTEMBER

M	T	W	T	F	S	S
						1
2	3	4	5	6	7	8
9	10	11	12	13	14	15
16	17	18	19	20	21	22
23	24	25	26	27	28	29
30						

OCTOBER

M	T	W	T	F	S	S
	1	2	3	4	5	6
7	8	9	10	11	12	13
14	15	16	17	18	19	20
21	22	23	24	25	26	27
28	29	30	31			

NOVEMBER

M	T	W	T	F	S	S
				1	2	3
4	5	6	7	8	9	10
11	12	13	14	15	16	17
18	19	20	21	22	23	24
25	26	27	28	29	30	

DECEMBER

M	T	W	T	F	S	S
						1
2	3	4	5	6	7	8
9	10	11	12	13	14	15
16	17	18	19	20	21	22
23	24	25	26	27	28	29
30	31					

December 2018 Week 52

24 Monday   ♋♌○

25 Tuesday   ♌○

26 Wednesday   ♌♍◑

27 Thursday   ♍◑

Week 52 December 2018

◐ ♍︎♎︎   Friday 28

◑ ♎︎   Saturday 29

◑ ♎︎   Sunday 30

This Week

This last week of the year leads up to a New Moon
eclipse next week so let go of anything negative!

New Moon Eclipse in Capricorn

It's the first New Moon of 2019. And it's an eclipse!

London	6 January	01:28
Sydney	6 January	12:28
Los Angeles	5 January	17:28

I t would be hard to find a more dramatic way to start this year (or this diary!) than with a New Moon eclipse. But that's what we're getting this week, in the sign of Capricorn.

Capricorn is already a super-charged sign because power planets Saturn and Pluto are also there (as is communications planet Mercury right now, too).

If you only do one New Moon wishing session this year (though that would be a shame!) do it this month. It's the start of the year and the New Moon eclipse is the perfect time to set out your intentions for the year ahead. This is going to be quite an intense eclipse because of the planetary alignments (and misalignments!) taking place just after the New Moon.

There's the possibility of self-doubt thanks to a Sun-Saturn connection, and hurtful words thanks to a Mercury-Chiron clash. That said, if you can talk your way to some kind of agreement, then a Mercury-Uranus link should allow you to turn around any situations that need fixing!

When you make your New Moon wishes, write them down and see if/where you feel in your heart: 'I doubt I can ever achieve this!' That's the planets showing you where you need to work harder on your goals and your self-belief.

☾ The Month Ahead

There could be some issues arising in the part of your chart being triggered, but they're just challenges to see how determined you are to make 2019 an amazing year. See p.11 for a quick guide to the Houses and read your Rising sign if you know it: Aries – 10th House; Taurus – 9th House; Gemini – 8th House; Cancer – 7th House; Leo – 6th House; Virgo – 5th House; Libra – 4th House; Scorpio – 3rd House; Sagittarius – 2nd House; Capricorn – 1st House; Aquarius – 12th House; Pisces – 11th House.

☾ Connect with Ganesh

As this is the first New Moon of the year, it's the right time to talk to the beautiful Hindu elephant god Ganesh. He'll help you to start anything new and also to overcome any obstacles, so ask him to be by your side as we move into 2019. Simply light a candle, gaze at an image of him and ask him to stay by your side.

New Moon Wishes and Intentions

Decide on your top 10 wishes and/or intentions for the coming four weeks. Be as specific or as vague as you like. Also decide what you can commit to doing, in order to make your wishes come true. If you like, visit my website to access a worksheet on which you can write your wish lists. You'll also find an audio guide to support you in the process.

_____

_____

_____

_____

_____

_____

_____

_____

Questions to Ask at This New Moon

What are my ambitions for the year ahead?

_____

_____

_____

_____

What does my dream job look like?

_____

_____

_____

_____

Have I been too hard on myself or anyone else?

_____

_____

_____

_____

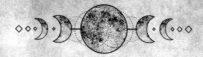

DEC/JAN WEEK 1

31 MONDAY ♎︎♏︎☽

1 TUESDAY ♏︎☽

2 WEDNESDAY ♐︎☽

3 THURSDAY ♐︎☽

● ♐ ♑   FRIDAY 4

● ♑   SATURDAY 5

● ♑ New Moon Eclipse 01:28   SUNDAY 6

THIS WEEK

The 6 January New Moon eclipse will
visible in eastern parts of Asia, the
Pacific and eastern Alaska, USA.

JANUARY WEEK 2

....

7 MONDAY   ≋ ◗

....

8 TUESDAY   ≋ ◗

....

9 WEDNESDAY   ≋)(◗

....

10 THURSDAY   )(◗

....

FRIDAY **11**

SATURDAY **12**

SUNDAY **13**

THIS WEEK

Once a month the Daily Moon moves into Aries, as it does this Saturday. Aries is the first sign of the zodiac, so this move marks the start of a new lunar cycle.

JANUARY WEEK 3

. . . .

14 MONDAY   ♈ ♉ ◑

. . . .

15 TUESDAY   ♉ ◑

. . . .

16 WEDNESDAY   ♉ ◑

. . . .

17 THURSDAY   ♊ ◑

. . . .

◯ ♊   FRIDAY **18**

◯ ♋   SATURDAY **19**

◯ ♋   SUNDAY **20**

THIS WEEK

Expect the energies to be extra high this week as we move towards a Full Moon eclipse. Just b-r-e-a-t-h-e.

Full Moon Eclipse in Leo

A time of huge energy!

London	21 January	05:16
Sydney	21 January	16:16
Los Angeles	20 January	21:16

This Full Moon eclipse is a real mixed bag! Full Moon eclipses are always a big deal as they ask us to turn a corner – they encourage us to move on. That's not something we're always keen to do (and I don't think that's just me!). Full Moon eclipses are also extra emotional. The Moon represents emotions in astrology, so when She swells to fullness, our emotions do too.

Moreover, this Full Moon eclipse is what you might call a 'doozy', since the first planetary alignment that takes place after it is a clash between angry Mars and strict Saturn. That sounds like an argument waiting to happen, especially if someone is trying to boss you around, or has some kind of authority over you.

Happily, just afterwards we get to kiss and make up under a far more alluring Venus-Jupiter link – this means love, and lots of it. If you're wondering about the most romantic night of the week, it's Monday (though Tuesday morning also looks pretty good!).

 The Month Ahead

Where are issues building up for you this month? There could be some drama in the part of your life being triggered, so stay focused on your goals. See p.11 for a quick guide to the Houses and read your Rising sign if you know it: Aries – 5th House; Taurus – 4th House; Gemini – 3rd House; Cancer – 2nd House; Leo – 1st House; Virgo – 12th House; Libra – 11th House; Scorpio – 10th House; Sagittarius – 9th House; Capricorn – 8th House; Aquarius – 7th House; Pisces – 6th House.

 Release Any Anger

Anger most certainly has its place: it means you're motivated. That said, this Full Moon could be quite emotional so take a deep breath and ask yourself if you have any anger issues you need to deal with. Once you've done so, take your mind from any anger and turn it towards peace. Here's a simple technique to help you:

1. Close your eyes and breathe gently.

2. As you breathe in, think the word 'peace' as you imagine the air (prana) coming in through the top of your head.

3. Then breathe out peace, too, through your nose or mouth, whichever feels more comfortable.

Full Moon Forgiveness List

Who do you need to forgive this month? Write out their name and then forgive them. They are more than likely doing their best, believe it or not!

_____

_____

_____

_____

_____

_____

_____

_____

_____

_____

_____

_____

☾ Questions to Ask at This Full Moon

Have I been too proud, or treating people like my servants?

_____

_____

_____

_____

Have I been acting like a diva? If so, why?

_____

_____

_____

_____

Am I allowing myself enough creative outlets?

_____

_____

_____

_____

JANUARY WEEK 4

21 MONDAY   **Full Moon Eclipse 05:16** ♌ ◯

22 TUESDAY   ♌ ◯

23 WEDNESDAY   ♍ ◗

24 THURSDAY   ♍ ◗

◐ ♎   FRIDAY 25

◑ ♎   SATURDAY 26

◑ ♏   SUNDAY 27

THIS WEEK

The Full Moon eclipse of 21 January
will be visible from Europe, Asia, Africa,
the Americas and the Arctic.

JANUARY WEEK 5

---

28 MONDAY

---

29 TUESDAY

---

30 WEDNESDAY

---

31 THURSDAY

WEEK 5　FEBRUARY

◐ ♄   FRIDAY **1**

Festivals of Imbolc (UK) and Lammas (Aus)

◑ ♄   SATURDAY **2**

● ♄ ≈   SUNDAY **3**

THIS WEEK

*In the northern hemisphere, 1 February brings
the festival of Imbolc. Down Under, with the
reversal of seasons, Lammas is celebrated.*

New Moon in Aquarius

The pressure is beginning to ease.

London	4 February	21:03
Sydney	5 February	08:03
Los Angeles	4 February	13:03

I f you feel like it's been a pretty intense start to the year, you're right, at least astrologically speaking. Not every year starts with two eclipses, but 2019 did! We had the New Moon eclipse in Capricorn then the Full Moon eclipse in Leo. And this week? We get another New Moon, but this time it's a regular lunation, not an eclipse. That means the pressure is off!

Moreover, this New Moon is harmoniously triggering Jupiter, the planet of good luck and good times. So if you need a restart on the year after the intense energies of the eclipses, give your confidence a boost (see opposite) and then go for it.

Also note that the New Moon in Aquarius always marks Chinese New Year. This year will be the year of the Earth Pig. The lucky colours of the year for those who follow the Chinese system will be red and white, which are said to balance the energy of the year of the pig. If you happen to have been born in the year of the pig, then you're advised to wear a red bracelet all year for good luck! Those years are 1935, 1947, 1959, 1971, 1983, 1995 and 2007, but double-check if you were born in January or February as if you were born before the New Moon in Aquarius in your birth year, you were born in the year of the dog.

The Month Ahead

This New Moon looks very friendly and kind, so whatever is happening in the part of your chart you read about should be very pleasant. See p.11 for a quick guide to the Houses and read your Rising sign if you know it: Aries – 11th House; Taurus – 10th House; Gemini – 9th House; Cancer – 8th House; Leo – 7th House; Virgo – 6th House; Libra – 5th House; Scorpio – 4th House; Sagittarius – 3rd House; Capricorn – 2nd House; Aquarius – 1st House; Pisces – 12th House.

Boost Your Confidence

This New Moon takes place just before a lovely Sun-Jupiter connection, which will help us all to feel more confident. Just after the New Moon, take an inventory of how you feel about your life and yourself: your love life, your work, your finances, your dreams and so on. Think about where you need more self-confidence and make a commitment to work on those areas in the coming month.

New Moon Wishes and Intentions

If the start of the year has been a bit too intense, use this New Moon to start all over again. Make your wishes and set your intentions like you haven't made any at all this year – freshly and with enthusiasm!

_____

_____

_____

_____

_____

_____

_____

_____

_____

_____

Questions to Ask at This New Moon

Have I been too detached lately? In which areas do I need to feel my feelings?

_____

_____

_____

_____

How could I do more to help others via charity or humanitarian work?

_____

_____

_____

When it comes to my most pressing issue, what's one totally new idea for resolving it?

_____

_____

_____

FEBRUARY WEEK 6

....

4 MONDAY   New Moon 21:03 ≋ ●

....

5 TUESDAY   ≋ ●

....

6 WEDNESDAY   )(●

....

7 THURSDAY   )(●

....

◐ ⟩ ♈   FRIDAY 8

◐ ♈   SATURDAY 9

◐ ♈   SUNDAY 10

THIS WEEK

'In the northern hemisphere it is the season of the waxing light,
post-Winter Solstice. In the southern hemisphere it is the season of
the waxing dark, post-Summer Solstice…' Dr Glenys Livingstone

FEBRUARY Week 7

11 MONDAY ♉ ◗

12 TUESDAY ♉ ◗

13 WEDNESDAY ♊ ◖

14 THURSDAY ♊ ○

◐ ♊ ♋   FRIDAY 15

○ ♋   SATURDAY 16

○ ♋ ♌   SUNDAY 17

THIS WEEK

This year's Valentine's Day takes place in the waxing cycle – good news for all the lovers out there!

Super Full Moon in Virgo

The high energies continue!

London	19 February	15:53
Sydney	20 February	02:53
Los Angeles	19 February	07:53

It's a good time of the year for Moon-watching, that's for sure. This week brings the Full Moon in Virgo, and it's a Supermoon – when the Moon's orbit is at perigee. This is Her closest point to the Earth, when She will appear up to 14 per cent bigger, but does all this have any real astrological significance? It's debatable.

Traditional astrology doesn't talk about Supermoons, but there is an argument to say that since the Moon controls the tides, and the Earth is just over 70 per cent water, we're affected when the Moon is closer. In theory, it could be a more intense Full Moon. You be the judge!

Full Moons in general and Supermoons in particular always are quite intense, but there is some very supportive astrology underlining this lunation.

For one thing, it's in mild Virgo, the sign that tends to be very reliable rather than dangerous. Moreover, Mercury

– the planet of the mind – is connecting to Saturn – the planet of stability and commitment – just after the Full Moon peaks. So even if this week feels a bit out of control with the strong lunar energies, you should feel like you're on stable ground afterwards.

 ## The Month Ahead

Here's where the Full Moon is triggering your chart. See p.11 for a quick guide to the Houses and read your Rising sign if you know it: Aries – 6th House; Taurus – 5th House; Gemini – 4th House; Cancer – 3rd House; Leo – 2nd House; Virgo – 1st House; Libra – 12th House; Scorpio – 11th House; Sagittarius – 10th House; Capricorn – 9th House; Aquarius – 8th House; Pisces – 7th House.

 ## It's Time to Declutter

One of the best things to do under the Virgo Full Moon, and especially with the steady Mercury-Saturn connection that follows, is to have a clear out. When it comes to keeping the energy in your home and your life moving, clutter is the enemy, . Decluttering comes very naturally to some people and less so to others (Cancerians especially, I'm looking at you!), so use this Full Moon to sort through those junk drawers and any piles of stuff under your bed. Amazing things happen when you get rid of the mess from your life.

Full Moon Forgiveness List

Remember that the Full Moon is the time to release negativity. One of the easiest ways to do that is to forgive and move on. Who do you need to forgive?

_____

_____

_____

_____

_____

_____

_____

_____

_____

☾ Questions to Ask at This Full Moon

Have I been too picky and critical of others?

_____

_____

_____

_____

Am I doing all I can to help others?

_____

_____

_____

_____

Have I been moaning rather than focusing on the positive?

_____

_____

_____

_____

FEBRUARY WEEK 8

....

18 MONDAY   ♌ ◯

....

19 TUESDAY   Full Moon 15:53 ♌♍ ◯

....

20 WEDNESDAY   ♍ ◯

....

21 THURSDAY   ♍♎ ◯

....

○♎   FRIDAY 22

○♎♏   SATURDAY 23

○♏   SUNDAY 24

This Week

The term 'Supermoon' was coined by US astrologer Richard Nolle in 1979. Reportedly he's tickled pink that his words went viral.

February Week 9

25 MONDAY ♏ ♐ ◑

26 TUESDAY ♐ ◑

27 WEDNESDAY ♐ ◑

28 THURSDAY ♑ ◑

WEEK 9 MARCH

FRIDAY 1

SATURDAY 2

SUNDAY 3

THIS WEEK

There's a lot of passion in the air thanks to a delicious Venus-Pluto link, so if you haven't seduced your lover in a while, this is the week to do so!

New Moon in Pisces

**If you want to be more intuitive, this is the week
to commit to working on your powers!**

London	6 March	16:03
Sydney	7 March	03:03
Los Angeles	6 March	08:03

If you're on the spiritual path (and you probably are if
you're using this diary!), then this is an important week
for you as it brings the New Moon in the spiritual and
psychic sign of Pisces. No matter which Star sign you are
or which sign you have rising, tap into the energies of this
New Moon if you're keen to boost your psychic abilities
and to tune more closely to the Divine.

That would be the case any and every year – the New
Moon in Pisces is amazing for elevating your heavenly
connections. However it goes triple this year as the New
Moon is actually taking place conjunct (in the same place
as) the planet strongly associated with Pisces – the planet
of the Divine, Neptune. So if you don't truly get your
Ommm on this week, you probably never will!

Moreover the New Moon and Neptune are both making

a harmonious link to the planet Saturn, so it's the ideal moment of the year to commit to some regular spiritual practice. Just having ideas such as *I should do more yoga…* or *I should meditate/chant more often…* is okay, but it's not the same as making a commitment to yourself and the Universe. Exercises like this can really make a difference, and your life will thank you as you incorporate regular practices that work for you.

The Month Ahead

New Moons like this don't come along every day of the year – they don't even come every year! Here's where the New Moon is triggering your chart. See p.11 for a quick guide to the Houses and read your Rising sign if you know it: Aries – 12th House; Taurus – 11th House; Gemini – 10th House; Cancer – 9th House; Leo – 8th House; Virgo – 7th House; Libra – 6th House; Scorpio – 5th House; Sagittarius – 4th House; Capricorn – 3rd House; Aquarius – 2nd House; Pisces – 1st House.

Commit to Your Spiritual Wellbeing

Think about a spiritual practice that lights you up and that you can commit to doing on a regular basis. It could be doing an oracle card reading, getting a massage, taking a yoga class, chanting, reading spiritual books, meditating, doing *chi gung* or anything else that helps you to feel connected.

New Moon Wishes and Intentions

Decide on your top 10 wishes and/or intentions for the coming four weeks. Be as specific or as vague as you like. Also decide what you can commit to doing, in order to make your wishes come true. If you like, visit my website to access a worksheet on which you can write your wish lists. You'll also find an audio guide to support you in the process.

_____

_____

_____

_____

_____

_____

_____

_____

_____

Questions to Ask at This New Moon

Am I giving and taking in equal amounts?

_____

_____

_____

_____

What is my big dream in life and what am I doing to achieve it?

_____

_____

_____

_____

Can I commit to daily meditation in the year ahead? If not, what can I commit to on a spiritual level?

_____

_____

_____

MARCH   WEEK 10

. . . .

4 MONDAY

. . . .

5 TUESDAY ♓☽

. . . .

6 WEDNESDAY   New Moon 16:03

. . . .

7 THURSDAY ♓♈●

. . . .

◐ ♈ FRIDAY 8

◐ ♈ SATURDAY 9

◐ ♉ SUNDAY 10

THIS WEEK

Mercury goes retrograde on 5 March so be sure you give yourself the space to think back over the past year and review how it was for you. Be grateful for all the good!

MARCH WEEK 11

....

11 MONDAY   ♉ 🌓

....

12 TUESDAY   ♉ ♊ 🌓

....

13 WEDNESDAY   ♊ 🌓

....

14 THURSDAY   ♊ ♋ 🌓

....

◐ ♋   FRIDAY **15**

○ ♋   SATURDAY **16**

○ ♌   SUNDAY **17**

THIS WEEK

*We're in the thick of the waxing cycle – make
the most of it by pursuing your dreams!*

Full Moon in Libra

This is the week to throw your emotional baggage overboard.

London	21 March	01:42
Sydney	21 March	12:42
Los Angeles	20 March	18:42

Most years we get one Full Moon in the sign of Libra. However, this year we get two, and this week brings the first. The Full Moon in Libra takes place when the Sun has moved into Libra's opposite sign of Aries and the Moon is now opposing the Sun from the sign of Libra.

As the first child (sign) of the zodiac, Aries is the 'Me! Me! Me!' sign. Libra, meanwhile, is the 'You! You! You!' sign, or you could call it the 'Us!' sign, since Libra is all about relationships.

Every Full Moon is about a tug-of-war of some kind that requires us to come into balance. It's also the ideal time to forgive and move on, as the Full Moon swells and our emotions come to the surface. Who do you need to forgive? You can access my Formula for Forgiveness at www. moonology.com/formula-for-forgiveness.

One of the best ways I know to use astrology and Moonology is to work on that part of our life associated with the sign that the New or Full Moon is in. On that basis, the Full Moon in Libra is the time to think about your relationships.

 ## The Month Ahead

There could be some drama in the part of your life being triggered, so stay focused on your goals. See p.11 for a quick guide to the Houses and read your Rising sign if you know it: Aries – 7th House; Taurus – 6th House; Gemini – 5th House; Cancer – 4th House; Leo – 3rd House; Virgo – 2nd House; Libra – 1st House; Scorpio – 12th House; Sagittarius – 11th House; Capricorn – 10th House; Aquarius – 9th House; Pisces – 8th House.

 ## March Equinox Ritual

We're at the changing of the seasons, no matter which hemisphere you're in. This is the time to rid yourself of anything or anyone that is holding you back.

1. Go outside, stand and just breathe.

2. Stretch up as high as you can and greet Father Sky.

3. Bend over and allow your hands to touch the ground and greet Mother Earth.

4. Spread your arms out wide to either side of you and declare out loud: 'This is the beginning!'

Full Moon Forgiveness List

Who do you need to forgive this month? Write out their name and then forgive them. They are more than likely doing their best, believe it or not!

_____

_____

_____

_____

_____

_____

_____

_____

_____

_____

Questions to Ask at This Full Moon

Am I willing to forgive and move on? (Remember that forgiving doesn't make what happened right, it just releases you!)

_____

_____

_____

Am I giving and taking in equal measure and if not, why not?

_____

_____

_____

Have I been too much in my head and not enough in my heart lately?

_____

_____

_____

MARCH WEEK 12

18 MONDAY ♌ ☽

19 TUESDAY ♍ ☽

20 WEDNESDAY ♍ ☽

Spring Equinox/Ostara (UK)

21 THURSDAY Full Moon 01:42 ♎ ○

Autumnal Equinox/Mabon (Aus)

○♎ FRIDAY 22

○♏ SATURDAY 23

○♏ SUNDAY 24

THIS WEEK

This week brings the Spring Equinox in the northern hemisphere . In the southern hemisphere it's the Autumnal Equinox, which falls at 08:58 (AEST) on 21 March.

MARCH WEEK 13

25 MONDAY ♐ ○

26 TUESDAY ♐ ☽

27 WEDNESDAY ♐ ♑ ☽

28 THURSDAY ♑ ☽

◐ ♄   FRIDAY 29

◐ ≈≈   SATURDAY 30

◐ ≈≈   SUNDAY 31

THIS WEEK

For anyone who follows Mercury retrograde,
Mercury ends its retrograde cycle on 28 March.
The next cycle begins in early July.

New Moon in Aries

The start of the new astrological and lunar cycle.

London	5 April	09:50
Sydney	5 April	19:50
Los Angeles	5 April	01:50

As you may know, Aries is the first sign of the zodiac. In the northern hemisphere, this makes total sense. The Sun and the New Moon are both in Aries at the time we get springtime. In fact it's the Sun's move into Aries, known as the 'Aries Ingress', that officially marks the end of winter and the start of spring. So it makes sense for Aries to be the start of the zodiac, since it's all about freshness, newness springing up, revitalization after a long, cold winter, our inner child and beginnings.

What this means for you is that if you have been on-again, off-again with your New and Full Moon practices and devotions so far this year, you have a second chance. Use this week's New Moon in Aries to make a commitment to working with the New and Full Moon every single month for the year ahead. It will change your life in ways you never thought possible.

So, get aligned with the cosmic energies and you'll start to see it's possible to manifest your dream life!

The Month Ahead

Here's where the Aries New Moon triggers your chart. See p.11 for a quick guide to the Houses and read your Rising sign if you know it: Aries – 1st House; Taurus – 12th House; Gemini – 11th House; Cancer – 10th House; Leo – 9th House; Virgo – 8th House; Libra – 7th House; Scorpio – 6th House; Sagittarius – 5th House; Capricorn – 4th House; Aquarius – 3rd House; Pisces – 2nd House.

Discipline Can Make Dreams Real

This week sees a gorgeous transition from a Mercury-Neptune (mind-dreams) connection to the New Moon to a Mercury-Saturn (mind-reality) alignment. New Moon weeks are always times to visualize your goals, but that goes triple this week because:

1. It's the first New Moon of the new lunar cycle.

2. There are Mercury-Neptune-Saturn conditions.

3. Visualization is one of the most powerful things to do at any time, but especially at a time like this!

Give yourself a good 5-15 minutes just to think about whatever it is that you want. Feel the love and gratitude this reality would bring you, then surrender your dreams to the Divine.

New Moon Wishes and Intentions

Decide on your top 10 wishes and/or intentions for the coming four weeks. Be as specific or as vague as you like. Also decide what you can commit to doing, in order to make your wishes come true. If you like, visit my website to access a worksheet on which you can write your wish lists. You'll also find an audio guide to support you in the process.

_____

_____

_____

_____

_____

_____

_____

_____

_____

Questions to Ask at This New Moon

Have I been selfish? Or do I need to be more selfish?

_____

_____

_____

Have I been overly competitive – do I need to tone it down? Or do I need to step up and go for what I want?

_____

_____

_____

_____

What is my one big commitment for the year ahead? Will I commit to monthly New and Full Moon practices?

_____

_____

_____

_____

APRIL WEEK 14

....

1 MONDAY   ≈ ⟩(◐

....

2 TUESDAY   ⟩(◐

....

3 WEDNESDAY   ⟩(◐

....

4 THURSDAY   ♈ ◑

....

● ♈ **New Moon 09:50**   FRIDAY **5**

● ♈ ♉   SATURDAY **6**

● ♉   SUNDAY **7**

THIS WEEK

*This week brings April Fools' Day. If you're wondering,
as I did when I began studying astrology, if it has any
astrological significance, the answer is no it doesn't. Its origin
is a mystery but one thing is sure – it's not astrological!*

APRIL WEEK 15

. . . .

8 MONDAY ♉ ♊ ◐

. . . .

9 TUESDAY ♊ ◐

. . . .

10 WEDNESDAY ♊ ◐

. . . .

11 THURSDAY ♋ ◐

. . . .

FRIDAY **12**

SATURDAY **13**

SUNDAY **14**

THIS WEEK

This is the first New Moon of the new lunar cycle, since Aries is the first sign of the zodiac. Commit now to working with all the New and Full Moons in the 12 months ahead and you'll work on every part of your life.

Full Moon in Libra

Let go of relationship upsets.

London	19 April	11:12
Sydney	19 April	21:12
Los Angeles	19 April	04:12

The second Full Moon in Libra reiterates the message of the first one a month ago. It's time to forgive and move on. For the astrologically curious, this Full Moon is a great moment to give you a slightly deeper understanding of how astrology and Moonology work.

Your astrological chart consists of a circle (360°) divided into 12 parts (the Houses). Using whole sign Houses, each of these Houses spans 30° and is ruled by a different sign. Usually, there is one Full Moon a month – bearing in mind that the Full Moon takes place when the Sun and Moon are on opposite sides of the zodiac. However this year, the first Full Moon in Libra took place at 0 degrees of Libra, and this second one is squeaking in at 29 degrees of Libra, hence the two Full Moons in succession in one year.

The significance is that we're all getting a second chance to work on our relationship issues. This Full Moon is the time to love with an open heart, but also to sever a relationship if you know it's doing you no good. But don't end it with anger. Tap into the beautiful and loving Libra energy and release this person with love, understanding that they were probably doing their best.

Immediately after the Full Moon the Moon goes Void of Course, which is an ideal time to meditate.

The Month Ahead

Here's where the Libra Full Moon triggers your chart. See p.11 for a quick guide to the Houses and read your Rising sign if you know it: Aries – 7th House; Taurus – 6th House; Gemini – 5th House; Cancer – 4th House; Leo – 3rd House; Virgo – 2nd House; Libra – 1st House; Scorpio – 12th House; Sagittarius – 11th House; Capricorn – 10th House; Aquarius – 9th House; Pisces – 8th House.

The Pink Bubble Visualization

This simple exercise will help you to release upsets:

1. Imagine the person you're forgiving in a pink bubble.

2. Smile at them and send them love.

3. Wave to them and wish them well as you see them floating away from you.

If you like to work with the angels, ask Archangel Michael to help you cut the cords with anyone you need to release from your life.

Full Moon Forgiveness List

Who do you need to forgive this month? Write out their name and then forgive them. They are more than likely doing their best, believe it or not!

_____

_____

_____

_____

_____

_____

_____

_____

_____

_____

Questions to Ask at This Full Moon

Am I holding on to a relationship for the wrong reasons?

_____

_____

_____

How can I find more balance between my life and my relationships?

_____

_____

_____

_____

Do I need to be more diplomatic at work and at home?

_____

_____

_____

_____

APRIL WEEK 16

....

15 MONDAY ♍ ☽

....

16 TUESDAY ♍ ☽

....

17 WEDNESDAY ♎ ○

....

18 THURSDAY ♎ ○

....

○ ♎ ♏ Full Moon 11:12   FRIDAY 19

○ ♏   SATURDAY 20

○ ♏ ♐   SUNDAY 21

THIS WEEK

The Libra Archangel is Jophiel. She has the rare power to help us to see the world through the eyes of beauty, so ask her to help you do that this week.

APRIL WEEK 17

....

22 MONDAY   ♐ 🌑

....

23 TUESDAY   ♐ ♑ 🌑

....

24 WEDNESDAY   ♑ 🌑

....

25 THURSDAY   ♑ 🌒

....

FRIDAY 26

SATURDAY 27

SUNDAY 28

THIS WEEK

Although this lunation brought the second Full Moon in Libra this year, it doesn't qualify as a Blue Moon (the name given to a second Full Moon within a calendar month).

New Moon in Taurus

Money can't buy happiness, but it can buy pretty things...

London	4 May	23:45
Sydney	5 May	08:45
Los Angeles	4 May	15:45

There is a misconception that in the West we're all madly money hungry, whereas in more 'spiritual' countries such as India, one of my favourite places to visit, everyone is more spiritually attuned and doesn't seek out cash. In my opinion, that's just a myth. We all need money – it's a grace and a Divine blessing, and something that we can attract or repel depending on how we feel about it.

The New Moon in the earthy sign of Taurus is a wonderful time to get clearer on your relationship with money. Do you want more? Or do you fear it's the root of all evil? There's some amazing astrology this month, so:

1. Go after what you want (Mercury/Mars).

2. Expect the best and attract it (Mercury/Jupiter).

3. Go after what you want even harder (Mars/Jupiter)!

Use this energy to recalibrate when it comes to stepping into the flow of abundance. I love the phrase inspired by Florence Scovel Shinn's work: 'I give excellent service for excellent pay!' This is powerful because if you know you're worth it, then you'll be more able to attract more money into your life to do the things you want to do.

The Month Ahead

Here's where the Moon is New for you in the month ahead. See p.11 for a quick guide to the Houses and read your Rising sign if you know it: Aries – 2nd House; Taurus – 1st House; Gemini – 12th House; Cancer – 11th House; Leo – 10th House; Virgo – 9th House; Libra – 8th House; Scorpio – 7th House; Sagittarius – 6th House; Capricorn – 5th House; Aquarius – 4th House; Pisces – 3rd House.

Create Good Financial Karma

To create good financial karma, commit to doing these three things for the coming year:

1. Give to charity.

2. Spend only what you can afford.

3. Make a budget and stick to it.

There is no magic bullet when it comes to money, but the Hindu goddess of abundance, Lakshmi, will listen to your prayers. Meditate on a picture of her, or make her your computer or phone screensaver.

New Moon Wishes and Intentions

Decide on your top 10 wishes and/or intentions for the coming four weeks. Be as specific or as vague as you like. Also decide what you can commit to doing, in order to make your wishes come true. If you like, visit my website to access a worksheet on which you can write your wish lists. You'll also find an audio guide to support you in the process.

_____

_____

_____

_____

_____

_____

_____

_____

_____

Questions to Ask at This New Moon

If I want more money, am I willing to devise a plan for getting it – and to stick to that plan?

How could I be more generous? (Generosity attracts abundance!)

Am I able to see money as a blessing that I can use for myself, my loved ones and also for charitable purposes?

APRIL/MAY WEEK 18

29 MONDAY ♓

....

30 TUESDAY ♓ 🌗

....

1 WEDNESDAY ♈ 🌑

Festivals of Beltane (UK) and Samhain (Aus)
....

2 THURSDAY ♈ 🌑

....

● ♈ ♉   FRIDAY 3

● ♉ New Moon 23:45   SATURDAY 4

● ♉   SUNDAY 5

THIS WEEK

In the northern hemisphere 1 May brings Beltane, the anglicized name for the Gaelic festival of May Day. It falls about halfway between the Spring Equinox and the Summer Solstice. In Australia, this week brings Samhain.

MAY WEEK 19

6 MONDAY   ♊ 🌑

7 TUESDAY   ♊ 🌒

8 WEDNESDAY   ♋ 🌒

9 THURSDAY   ♋ 🌓

◗ ♋♌   FRIDAY 10

◗ ♌   SATURDAY 11

◗ ♌♍   SUNDAY 12

THIS WEEK

This New Moon connects beautifully to Neptune, the
planet of dreams and visions. After you've made your
New Moon wishes, do a meditation and pay attention
to any ethereal messages that come through.

Full Moon in Scorpio

It's time to let go of grudges.

London	18 May	22:11
Sydney	19 May	07:11
Los Angeles	18 May	14:11

Once in a Blue Moon we have the chance to let go of our upsets and boost our bank balance in the same week, and this is one of those Blue Moons! There are various definitions of a Blue Moon – in this case, it's because this is the third Full Moon in a season with four Full Moons. So what to do with a Moon that's Blue? Use it to:

1. Go deep (Scorpio is all about going deeper) into your heart and think about if and where you have any upsets or distress you need to release, and whether you need to forgive someone (or yourself).

2. Let go of fear, especially fear you may have around money. Just after the Full Moon comes a stunning Venus-Uranus connection which could be great for turning your finances around – assuming you believe that's possible!

3. Realize that loving people is much easier than being upset with them. They are more than likely doing their best!

☽ The Month Ahead

Here's where this lunation is triggering your chart. See p.11 for a quick guide to the Houses and read your Rising sign if you know it: Aries – 8th House; Taurus – 7th House; Gemini – 6th House; Cancer – 5th House; Leo – 4th House; Virgo – 3rd House; Libra – 2nd House; Scorpio – 1st House; Sagittarius – 12th House; Capricorn – 11th House; Aquarius – 10th House; Pisces – 9th House.

☽ Full Moon Forgiveness and Karma Release

If you only use the Full Moon forgiveness formula (*see p.5*) once this year, make sure that time is now. It's ideal to use at any Full Moon, but especially a Scorpio Blue Moon. Why? Because forgiveness is what releases karma and Scorpio often finds it hard to release. Before you judge Scorpios, remember that we all have Scorpio somewhere in our chart. That's just how astrology works.

The Scorpio Full Moon every year is the time to let go of upsets. Full Moon time is moving-on time. Break the karma between you and whomever you think wronged you. By releasing your grip, you will actually be setting yourself free.

Staying stuck in upset or anger only ties to you to the past, and it's here in the present that you create your future.

Full Moon Forgiveness List

Who do you need to forgive this month? Write out their name
and then forgive them. They are more than likely doing their best,
believe it or not!

_____

_____

_____

_____

_____

_____

_____

_____

Questions to Ask at This Full Moon

Think of someone you're upset with and ask yourself: what does it do for me, to hold on to this anger? What would releasing the upset do for me?

_____

_____

_____

_____

What fears do I have around money?

_____

_____

_____

Where do my fears around money come from?

_____

_____

_____

_____

MAY WEEK 20

. . . .

13 MONDAY ♍︎☽

. . . .

14 TUESDAY ♍︎♎︎☽

. . . .

15 WEDNESDAY ♎︎☽

. . . .

16 THURSDAY ♎︎♏︎☽

. . . .

◯ ♏︎   FRIDAY 17

◯ ♏︎ Full Moon 22:11   SATURDAY 18

◯ ♐︎   SUNDAY 19

THIS WEEK

This week brings Wesak (19 May), the most important
festival in the Buddhist calendar, marking the birth,
enlightenment and death of Lord Buddha.

MAY WEEK 21

20 MONDAY ♐ ○

21 TUESDAY ♑ ○

22 WEDNESDAY ♑ ○

23 THURSDAY ♑ ♒ ◑

◐ ≋   Friday 24

◐ ≋   Saturday 25

◑ ⊬   Sunday 26

This Week

*Last week brought the only Blue Moon of 2019 – this
is your last chance to tune in to Her energies!*

MAY WEEK 22

27 MONDAY   ♓ ☽

28 TUESDAY   ♓♈ ☽

29 WEDNESDAY   ♈ ☽

30 THURSDAY   ♈ ☽

● ♉   FRIDAY **31**

● ♉   SATURDAY **1**

● ♊   SUNDAY **2**

THIS WEEK

By the end of this week we're at the very end of the
waning cycle so take it super-easy if you can.

New Moon in Gemini

This is a week where one conversation could change everything!

London	3 June	11:01
Sydney	3 June	20:01
Los Angeles	3 June	03:01

If you wanted to make a sentence from the keywords for this week's New Moon, it could be: Use your mind (Gemini/Mercury) to turn your life around (Uranus).

The New Moon this week takes place just ahead of a lovely link between Mercury and Uranus. Saturn and Neptune are also approaching an alignment (peaking June 18, but already in the ethers), which is perfect for making dreams (Neptune) real (Saturn). There could even be some second chances coming up, since Saturn is retrograding at the same time. However, note that some effort could be required to see through the 'maya', or illusion, to the truth, since the first alignment that the Moon makes after the New Moon is a clash with confusing Neptune.

The annual New Moon in Gemini is also the perfect time to think about... how you're thinking. As my teacher

Narayani Amma says, 'Good thoughts lead to good actions which lead to good karma!' Thinking positively is not about pretending everything is okay when it's not. We all need to process stuff, but we need to process it and then release it!

 ## The Month Ahead

Here's where the New Moon is triggering your chart. See p.11 for a quick guide to the Houses and read your Rising sign if you know it: Aries – 3rd House; Taurus – 2nd House; Gemini – 1st House; Cancer – 12th House; Leo – 11th House; Virgo – 10th House; Libra – 9th House; Scorpio – 8th House; Sagittarius – 7th House; Capricorn – 6th House; Aquarius – 5th House; Pisces – 4th House.

 ## The 'Dismiss!' Technique

I've been using this technique for many years as a way to throw bad stuff, negative thoughts and general stagnant energy out of my auric field.

If and when you think a fearful thought that you don't want to manifest, recognize it as fear and then place the fingers of your right hand between your breasts, before throwing your hand away from your body as far as you can with the word 'Dismiss!'

The idea is not to allow the fear to percolate in your heart where it can turn from a thought-form to reality. We all have negative thoughts, and it's important to acknowledge them and see them for what they are – fear. And then to dismiss them from our energy field.

New Moon Wishes and Intentions

Decide on your top 10 wishes and/or intentions for the coming four weeks. Be as specific or as vague as you like. Also decide what you can commit to doing, in order to make your wishes come true. If you like, visit my website to access a worksheet on which you can write your wish lists. You'll also find an audio guide to support you in the process.

_____

_____

_____

_____

_____

_____

_____

_____

_____

_____

Questions to Ask at This New Moon

How can I commit to focusing on solutions rather than problems in the year ahead?

_____

_____

Is there someone I need to have a good talk to – can I commit to doing that this week under the communicative Gemini New Moon?

_____

_____

What are my main objectives for the rest of the year?

_____

_____

_____

_____

_____

_____

JUNE WEEK 23

....

3 MONDAY   New Moon 11:01 ♊ 🌑

....

4 TUESDAY   ♊♋ 🌑

....

5 WEDNESDAY   ♋ 🌑

....

6 THURSDAY   ♋♌ 🌑

....

◑ ♌   FRIDAY **7**

◑ ♌ ♍   SATURDAY **8**

◑ ♍   SUNDAY **9**

THIS WEEK

On 5 June, the United Nations aims to create worldwide awareness of the environment with World Environment Day. What can you do to make your own environment – your home, your neighbourhood – a better place?

JUNE WEEK 24

....

10 MONDAY   ♍ ◗

....

11 TUESDAY   ♎ ◑

....

12 WEDNESDAY   ♎ ◑

....

13 THURSDAY   ♏ ◖

....

○♏ FRIDAY **14**

○♐ SATURDAY **15**

○♐ SUNDAY **16**

THIS WEEK

Next week brings the solstice – the longest (northern hemisphere) or the shortest (southern hemisphere) day of the year. Can you feel a turning point coming?

Full Moon in Sagittarius

Make your dreams real under the Full Moon...

London	17 June	09:30
Sydney	17 June	18:30
Los Angeles	17 June	01:30

It's a Full Moon week so prepare for some heightened emotions. The good news is that this Full Moon is straddling two of the less emotional signs – Gemini and Sagittarius. Not that Gemini and Sagittarius don't emote with the best of them, they just tend to be less dramatic when it comes to their feelings. Gemini is an Air sign and is a lot in its head, and Sagittarius is a Fire sign, well known for its sense of humour.

The Full Moon this week in happy-go-lucky Sagittarius is very positive overall. There's a sense that if you're moving on from something, as so often happens at the time of a Full Moon, you'll be moving on with a smile and looking forward to the next adventure.

Also note there's a still-building Saturn-Neptune connection under this Full Moon. Saturn is the planet of reality and facts while Neptune is the planet of dreams.

When these two planets clash, dreams can be crushed. However, when they combine harmoniously, as they're doing this week, there really is a sense that dreams can come true, especially if you're willing to put in the hard work required.

 ## The Month Ahead

Here's where the Full Moon is for you. See p.11 for a quick guide to the Houses and read your Rising sign if you know it: Aries – 9th House; Taurus – 8th House; Gemini – 7th House; Cancer – 6th House; Leo – 5th House; Virgo – 4th House; Libra – 3rd House; Scorpio – 2nd House; Sagittarius – 1st House; Capricorn – 12th House; Aquarius – 11th House; Pisces – 10th House.

 ## Thoughts for the Solstice

At the time of the solstice, take a moment to think about what is coming up in the months ahead.

In the northern hemisphere, it's all about the height of summer. Down Under, of course, it's about being half way through winter. Wherever you are in the world, lighting a candle is a symbol of the celebration.

In the northern climes, an orange, red or yellow candle symbolizes the Sun burning brightly for summer. It's said you should leave the candle burning all day long.

In the southern hemisphere, the same coloured candle symbolizes the warmth of hearth and home as winter peaks, and also reminds us of the coming of the light at the end of the coldest months.

Full Moon Forgiveness List

Who do you need to forgive this month? Write out their name and then forgive them. They are more than likely doing their best, believe it or not!

_____

_____

_____

_____

_____

_____

_____

_____

_____

Questions to Ask at This Full Moon

Do I understand that believing I'm lucky makes me luckier?

_____

_____

_____

_____

Am I willing to do a Lakshmi chant, *Om Shri Lakshmi Namaha*, every day until the New Moon to increase my luck?

_____

_____

_____

When have I been flippant or careless lately?

_____

_____

_____

_____

JUNE WEEK 25

....

17 MONDAY   Full Moon 09:30 ♐ ♑ ○

....

18 TUESDAY   ♑ ○

....

19 WEDNESDAY   ♑ ○

....

20 THURSDAY   ♒ ◑

....

  FRIDAY **21**

Summer Solstice/Litha (UK)

SATURDAY 22

Winter Solstice (Aus)

SUNDAY 23

THIS WEEK

In the northern hemisphere, this week brings the
Summer Solstice on 21 June. In the southern
hemisphere, it's the Winter Solstice on 22 June.

JUNE WEEK 26

....

24 MONDAY   ♓︎ ◑

....

25 TUESDAY   ♈︎ ◑

....

26 WEDNESDAY   ♈︎ ◑

....

27 THURSDAY   ♈︎♉︎ ◑

....

● ♉   FRIDAY 28

● ♉ ♊   SATURDAY 29

● ♊   SUNDAY 30

THIS WEEK

The Quarter Moon this week triggers healing
Chiron – what needs healing in your life?

New Moon Eclipse in Cancer

An eclipse, and Mercury goes retrograde!

London	2 July	20:16
Sydney	3 July	05:16
Los Angeles	2 July	12:16

So here we are at the first eclipse of the season. This week brings the New Moon eclipse, and in two weeks' time we'll get the Full Moon eclipse. New Moon eclipses are like New Moons on steroids. In other words, while New Moons have traditionally been the time to make wishes, cast spells and set intentions, New Moon eclipses are that and so much more.

This month's eclipse takes place in the super-emotional sign of Cancer, so we can expect very high energies and to feel all our feelings this week. Water signs and Capricorns in particular could be especially emotional.

This eclipse is also aided by communications planet Mercury, which is going into a new retrograde cycle in the sign of Leo. If you know where Leo is in your chart, that is where you need to do some rethinking, reviewing and maybe even some revisiting.

In the past, people feared eclipses, as suddenly the sky went dark (in the case of a Solar Eclipse), the birds stopped chirping and the dogs started barking. But now we know better, so don't fear the eclipse and instead work with it and the Mercury reverse cycle.

Soon after the eclipse this week we get a Mercury-Mars meeting. This could translate quite easily into the idea of 'S/he who dares under this New Moon, wins!'

The Month Ahead

Here's where the New Moon is for you. See p.11 for a quick guide to the Houses and read your Rising sign if you know it: Aries – 4th House; Taurus – 3rd House; Gemini – 2nd House; Cancer – 1st House; Leo – 12th House; Virgo – 11th House; Libra – 10th House; Scorpio – 9th House; Sagittarius – 8th House; Capricorn – 7th House; Aquarius – 6th House; Pisces – 5th House.

Set Your Intentions

I'm hoping that you've been doing your New Moon wishes every month without fail. After all, if you want to change your life, you have to get really clear in your intentions.

That said, life does happen, events sometimes get in the way and every now and then, despite the best of intentions, we don't do what we mean to do. But this week? This week I implore you! It's the New Moon eclipse, which makes it one of the most powerful times in 2019 to make your wishes and set your intentions.

New Moon Wishes and Intentions

Decide on your top 10 wishes and/or intentions for the coming four weeks. Be as specific or as vague as you like. Also decide what you can commit to doing, in order to make your wishes come true. If you like, visit my website to access a worksheet on which you can write your wish lists. You'll also find an audio guide to support you in the process.

_____

_____

_____

_____

_____

_____

_____

_____

_____

Questions to Ask at This New Moon

Am I happy in my home and if not, what am I going to do about it?

_____

_____

_____

What are my wishes for myself and my family in the coming six months?

_____

_____

_____

_____

Have I been going at my goals sideways, and do I need to be more direct?

_____

_____

_____

JULY WEEK 27

1 MONDAY ♊ ●

2 TUESDAY **New Moon Eclipse 20:16** ♋ ●

3 WEDNESDAY ♋ ●

4 THURSDAY ♌ ●

FRIDAY 5

SATURDAY 6

SUNDAY 7

THIS WEEK

*Eclipses are such important times to stay conscious
and there's a New Moon eclipse this week. Also
note that Mercury goes retrograde on 8 July.*

JULY WEEK 28

8 MONDAY   ♎ ◗

9 TUESDAY   ♎ ◑

10 WEDNESDAY   ♏ ◖

11 THURSDAY   ♏ ◖

○ ♏︎ ♐︎   FRIDAY **12**

○ ♐︎   SATURDAY **13**

○ ♐︎ ♑︎   SUNDAY **14**

THIS WEEK

*If life feels a bit crazy now, just increase your meditation,
yoga or chanting practice. We're in eclipse season!*

Full Moon Eclipse in Capricorn

Let it go – especially work dramas!

London	16 July	22:38
Sydney	17 July	07:38
Los Angeles	16 July	14:38

This Full Moon eclipse week is looking mighty intense, thanks to a line-up of planets facing off on either side of the sky. The Sun is in Cancer, and the Moon is opposing the Sun in the sign of work-oriented Capricorn. Huddled around both luminaries we have a veritable celestial tangle.

In addition to the Moon are the south node, Saturn and Pluto in the sign of Capricorn. The lunar nodes are the points at which the orbit of the Moon crosses the ecliptic. The South Node is associated with our obsessions. It's about where we've come from – past lives even. Saturn and Pluto are about lessons and power, and are both extremely intense planets: Saturn is the immovable object, while Pluto is the unstoppable force. Right now they're very near each other and the energies are building.

On the other side of the sky, and opposing all of this – literally acting like provocateurs – are the Sun, Mercury, Venus, Mars and the north node in Cancer. The North Node is about where we need to go in order to find happiness and fulfilment. The Sun is the ego, Mercury is the trickster, Venus is the lover and Mars is the fighter. In addition, this celestial action is taking place under an eclipse, and a Full Moon eclipse involving emotional Cancer at that!

This is such a hot combination that it's a week to live consciously. Look at what you need to release. It could be a person, a job or a situation, or it could be a feeling you're clinging on to that is doing you no good.

 ## The Month Ahead

Here's where the eclipse is for you. See p.11 for a quick guide to the Houses and read your Rising sign if you know it: Aries – 10th House; Taurus – 9th House; Gemini – 8th House; Cancer – 7th House; Leo – 6th House; Virgo – 5th House; Libra – 4th House; Scorpio – 3rd House; Sagittarius – 2nd House; Capricorn – 1st House; Aquarius – 12th House; Pisces – 11th House.

 ## Think about Your Spiritual Teacher

Amid eclipse-week madness, when anything could happen and probably will, falls the Hindu festival of Guru Purnima on 16 July. It's also celebrated by Buddhists and a day when we, as students of life, honour our spiritual teachers, or gurus, and send them love and gratitude.

Full Moon Forgiveness List

Who do you need to forgive this month? Write out their name and then forgive them. They are more than likely doing their best, believe it or not!

_____

_____

_____

_____

_____

_____

_____

_____

_____

Questions to Ask at This Full Moon

Who has been my greatest teacher and why?

_____

_____

_____

_____

What wisdom have I learned that I can pass on?

_____

_____

_____

_____

Which work dramas am I now willing to leave behind?

_____

_____

_____

_____

July Week 29

15 Monday ♉︎ ○

16 Tuesday Full Moon Eclipse 22:38 ♉︎ ◑

17 Wednesday ♒︎ ○

18 Thursday ♒︎ ○

◯ ≈ ♓   FRIDAY 19

◯ ♓   SATURDAY 20

◗ ♓   SUNDAY 21

THIS WEEK

*This week's partial lunar eclipse will be partly visible in parts
of Europe and Asia, Australia, Africa, the Americas and
Antarctica, and the Pacific, Atlantic and Indian oceans.*

JULY WEEK 30

22 MONDAY ♈︎ ◯

23 TUESDAY ♈︎ ◗

24 WEDNESDAY ♈︎ ♉︎ ◗

25 THURSDAY ♉︎ ◐

◗ ♉   FRIDAY 26

◗ ♊   SATURDAY 27

◗ ♊   SUNDAY 28

THIS WEEK

*Time to breathe… we're now officially
out of the eclipse season.*

New Moon in Leo

Be proud – but not too proud!

London	1 August	04:11
Sydney	1 August	13.11
Los Angeles	31 July	20.11

We need to watch out that pride doesn't come before a fall this week. As you might know, Leo is the sign of the lion, king of the jungle and lord of his pride. Wherever we have Leo in our chart (*see opposite*) is where we have something we can be proud of. Think about that part of your life and whether you really are proud of it. If not, what can you do to change that?

While a bit of pride is a good thing, too much, of course, is the opposite. That's the risk this week with the New Moon in Leo, just ahead of a Sun-Venus-Uranus clash. There could be a few egos out of joint, money surprises or love matters that you didn't see coming. Whatever happens, keep asking yourself whether you're allowing your pride to get in the way. This New Moon also offers fantastic creative opportunities... a breakthrough, perhaps, or a new, more creative approach to something.

When the planet of change, Uranus, is triggered as it has been this week, your best bet is always to make your motto: 'Live and let live'. The more you try to control things, the more trouble you're likely to get yourself into.

 ## The Month Ahead

Here's where Leo is for you, and where the New Moon is triggering your chart. See p.11 for a quick guide to the Houses and read your Rising sign if you know it: Aries – 5th House; Taurus – 4th House; Gemini – 3rd House; Cancer – 2nd House; Leo – 1st House; Virgo – 12th House; Libra – 11th House; Scorpio – 10th House; Sagittarius – 9th House; Capricorn – 8th House; Aquarius – 7th House; Pisces – 6th House.

 ## Thank You, Mother Earth

With the celebrations of Lammas in the northern hemisphere and Imbolc Down Under, now is a good time to honour the changing seasons. Here's a dedication you might like to use:

Thank you, Mother Earth, for the changing seasons that measure out my life.

May I always celebrate as the Earth turns, from day to night and back to day, from summer to autumn to spring to winter, and back again.

As I grow with each day and each season, I honour you as you honour me.

New Moon Wishes and Intentions

Decide on your top 10 wishes and/or intentions for the coming four weeks. Be as specific or as vague as you like. Also decide what you can commit to doing, in order to make your wishes come true. If you like, visit my website to access a worksheet on which you can write your wish lists. You'll also find an audio guide to support you in the process.

_____

_____

_____

_____

_____

_____

_____

_____

_____

_____

Questions to Ask at This New Moon

What bounty do I need to take time to be grateful for?

_____

_____

_____

_____

Have I been proud of myself in a good way – or just too proud?

_____

_____

_____

How well am I treating the people in my life?

_____

_____

_____

_____

JULY/AUGUST WEEK 31

. . . .

29 MONDAY Ⅱ♋

. . . .

30 TUESDAY ♋

. . . .

31 WEDNESDAY ♋♌ ●

. . . .

1 THURSDAY New Moon 04:11 ♌ ●

. . . .

Festivals of Lammas (UK) and Imbolc (Aus)

● ♌︎♍︎   FRIDAY 2

● ♍︎   SATURDAY 3

● ♍︎♎︎   SUNDAY 4

THIS WEEK

Mercury ends its retrograde cycle on 1 August,
pretty much the world over. It started in
Leo and moved back into Cancer.

AUGUST WEEK 32

---

5 MONDAY

---

6 TUESDAY

---

7 WEDNESDAY

---

8 THURSDAY

○ ♐   FRIDAY 9

○ ♐   SATURDAY 10

○ ♑   SUNDAY 11

THIS WEEK

We're in the waxing cycle again, so make sure you
go for it in terms of chasing your dreams.

Full Moon in Aquarius

Feel your feelings, but not too much…

London	15 August	13:29
Sydney	15 August	22:29
Los Angeles	15 August	05:29

The week ahead brings a weird combination of astrological energies. On the one hand we have the Full Moon, which, as you'll have gathered by now, is a time when we get more emotional – the Moon swells to fullness, and more Moon equals more emotions. This month, however, the Full Moon is in the rather more detached, aloof sign of Aquarius, so you can expect some heightened emotions, but also expect to be able to rise above your feelings (hopefully in a good way).

Added to this is the fact that at the time of the Full Moon, the Sun will be conjunct (in the same place as) the planet of love and abundance, Venus. In addition, the planet of sex and drive, Mars, is also very close by.

All in all, there is a sense that the ego is on fire, love is in the air, love issues are rising up and tempers are also possibly rising – but if we decide to, we can detach from everything and cruise through the week. Hopefully! If you do your regular Full Moon forgiveness and negativity release practice, the slightly cooler emotional temperature should make it easier for you to do some real releasing, so spend some time cutting your emotional ties with the past. The week's Mercury-Chiron link will also help this process.

 ## The Month Ahead

Here's where the Full Moon is for you. See p.11 for a quick guide to the Houses and read your Rising sign if you know it: Aries – 11th House; Taurus – 10th House; Gemini – 9th House; Cancer – 8th House; Leo – 7th House; Virgo – 6th House; Libra – 5th House; Scorpio – 4th House; Sagittarius – 3rd House; Capricorn – 2nd House; Aquarius – 1st House; Pisces – 12th House.

 ## Release Your Negative Energy

Energetically, this is a fantastic week for a negativity release ritual. The Moon represents the unconscious, but when She is full, the unknown becomes known, the unconscious becomes conscious and the hidden is finally revealed. If we don't like what we see, we must bring light to our dark side.

To do that you must first acknowledge your dark side, so write down what you're upset about. Where have you let yourself down? Where have you allowed your standards to slip? What do you need to let go of? Write it all down. Then say, "I now release all negativity, anything that doesn't support my highest good.'

Full Moon Forgiveness List

Who do you need to forgive this month? Write out their name
and then forgive them. They are more than likely doing their best,
believe it or not!

_____

_____

_____

_____

_____

_____

_____

_____

_____

Questions to Ask at This Full Moon

Am I willing to shake off anything (or anyone) that stops me from being authentic?

_____

_____

_____

When I focus on love, what comes to mind?

_____

_____

_____

_____

Can I get out of my head and into my heart?

_____

_____

_____

_____

AUGUST WEEK 33

. . . .

12 MONDAY ♑☽

. . . .

13 TUESDAY ♑♒☽

. . . .

14 WEDNESDAY ♒☽

. . . .

15 THURSDAY   Full Moon 13:29 ♒○

. . . .

○ ♓   Friday **16**

○ ♓   Saturday **17**

○ ♓ ♈   Sunday **18**

This Week

*A Mercury-Uranus clash on 16–17 August could mean
some conversations spiral out of control. Go easy, since
the Full Moon already brings heightened emotions.*

AUGUST WEEK 34

19 MONDAY   ♈○

20 TUESDAY   ♈○

21 WEDNESDAY   ♉◐

22 THURSDAY   ♉◑

◐ ♉ ♊   FRIDAY 23

◑ ♊   SATURDAY 24

◑ ♊ ♋   SUNDAY 25

THIS WEEK

*Every Full Moon sees a tug-of-war between the signs
straddled by the Sun and the Moon. In the case of the
Aquarius Full Moon, it's about finding a balance between
trying to be all things to all people vs having real relationships.*

New Moon in Virgo

Change is in the air. Are you ready?

London	30 August	11:37
Sydney	30 August	20:37
Los Angeles	30 August	03:37

What springs to mind looking at the ephemeris (book of the planets) for this Full Moon is that the changemaker planet, Uranus, is grabbing all the headlines.

Uranus, the planet of chaos, makes four major connections this week: with Venus, Mars, the Sun and then Mercury. Uranus takes around 84 years to orbit the Sun, and spends around seven years in each sign. Last year it moved out of Aries and into Taurus, stirring up the money markets and cryptocurrencies. Taurus and Virgo are both Earth signs and are therefore 'friends'. Venus and Mars are also both in Virgo, the sign where this week's New Moon is taking place. This means that:

1. This week looks pretty good overall.

2. Life should mostly flow quite easily.

3. There could be ups and downs, but likely more ups.

4. There could be major turnarounds and radical reversals.

5. When it comes to love, sex and in particular abundance, change awaits.

Where does this leave your New Moon practice? It means you need to gather up all your intentions, send them out to the Universe and declare, 'For the good of all, or not at all!' Big changes are possible now, so make sure you know what you want. Virgo is known as a rather meek and mild sign, but the energies of this New Moon mean that even the mild-mannered will find the words to declare our desires!

 The Month Ahead

Here's where the New Moon is triggering for you. See p.11 for a quick guide to the Houses and read your Rising sign if you know it: Aries – 6th House; Taurus – 5th House; Gemini – 4th House; Cancer – 3rd House; Leo – 2nd House; Virgo – 1st House; Libra – 12th House; Scorpio – 11th House; Sagittarius – 10th House; Capricorn – 9th House; Aquarius – 11th House; Pisces – 10th House.

Bring Good Karma

One of the most wonderful ways to bring good karma into your life is to do good things for others. Of all the zodiac signs, Virgo is the sign of service and loves to help, so at the time of the Full Moon, do a random act of kindness for a friend, a family member or a stranger. See how good it feels, and maybe you'll feel encouraged to do more.

New Moon Wishes and Intentions

Decide on your top 10 wishes and/or intentions for the coming four weeks. Be as specific or as vague as you like. Also decide what you can commit to doing, in order to make your wishes come true. If you like, visit my website to access a worksheet on which you can write your wish lists. You'll also find an audio guide to support you in the process.

_____

_____

_____

_____

_____

_____

_____

_____

_____

_____

☾ Questions to Ask at This New Moon

If what goes around comes around, what help can I offer someone to get the help I need in return?

_____

_____

_____

How can I improve my health? (Virgo is all about health.)

_____

_____

_____

_____

Where in my life could I be more organized? (Begin it now!)

_____

_____

_____

_____

AUGUST WEEK 35

. . . .

26 MONDAY   ♋ 🌓

. . . .

27 TUESDAY   ♋♌ 🌓

. . . .

28 WEDNESDAY   ♌ 🌓

. . . .

29 THURSDAY   ♌ 🌓

. . . .

New Moon 11:37

FRIDAY 30

SATURDAY 31

SUNDAY 1

THIS WEEK

This New Moon is a biggie! It's a Black Moon
(the second New Moon in single calendar month) and
a Supermoon, so don't waste it – make your wishes!

SEPTEMBER Week 36

2 MONDAY ♎ 🌔

3 TUESDAY ♏ 🌔

4 WEDNESDAY ♏ 🌔

5 THURSDAY ♐ 🌓

◐ ♐   FRIDAY 6

◐ ♑   SATURDAY 7

◐ ♑   SUNDAY 8

THIS WEEK

*This week's alignment of three planets plus the Sun
and the Moon is striking! Double-check where the
New Moon is triggering for you – that's a power
centre and an energetic hotspot for you now.*

Full Moon in Pisces

Behold, a Micromoon!

London	14 September	05:32
Sydney	14 September	14:32
Los Angeles	13 September	21:32

You've heard of a Supermoon. That's when the New or Full Moon takes place at perigee – the time of the month when the Moon is closest to the Earth and appears up to 14 per cent bigger. But what about a Micromoon? As you might guess, this is when the New or Full Moon takes place at apogee – when the Moon is as far as She gets from the Earth during her monthly cycle. That's what we have this week.

There's not much research into whether or not people feel a Supermoon more or a Micromoon less. However, based on the idea that humans are 70 per cent water and the Moon controls the tides, there is a basis to say that we should at least feel more at a Supermoon and less at a Micromoon. You can be the judge this week.

Whatever else you do, be sure to complete your Full Moon forgiveness practice this week. Which negatives do you want to release? Write them down! We're now well into the second half of the year, and if you've been doing your New and Full Moon work all year you should be starting to feel real changes.

☾ The Month Ahead

Here's where the Micromoon will affect your chart. See p.11 for a quick guide to the Houses and read your Rising sign if you know it: Aries – 12th House; Taurus – 11th House; Gemini – 10th House; Cancer – 9th House; Leo – 8th House; Virgo – 7th House; Libra – 6th House; Scorpio – 5th House; Sagittarius – 4th House; Capricorn – 3rd House; Aquarius – 2nd House; Pisces – 1st House.

☾ Create Balance for Wellbeing

Every Full Moon brings a tug-of-war between the qualities of the two signs that the Full Moon is straddling (remember, a Full Moon takes place when the Sun and Moon are exactly opposite each other in the sky). At this Full Moon, the Sun is in Virgo while the Moon is in Pisces. That means it's time to find a balance between your duties and your need for inner peace.

Take a moment to make a list of all your weekly duties – anything from seeing your parents to ferrying your kids around to taking out the recycling, and so on. Make sure your schedule is workable. Then find 20 minutes at least three times a week for yoga, meditation, chanting or another form of relaxation, and add that to your schedule.

Full Moon Forgiveness List

Who do you need to forgive this month? Write out their name and then forgive them. They are more than likely doing their best, believe it or not!

_____

_____

_____

_____

_____

_____

_____

_____

_____

_____

Questions to Ask at This Full Moon

Have I had my head in the clouds? If so, how do I ground myself?

_____

_____

_____

_____

Have I been a martyr, or cut off my nose to spite my face?

_____

_____

_____

Can I commit to daily meditation to boost my intuition and connection to my higher self?

_____

_____

_____

_____

SEPTEMBER WEEK 37

9 MONDAY ♑ ≈ 🌑

10 TUESDAY ≈ 🌑

11 WEDNESDAY ≈ 🌑

12 THURSDAY ♓ 🌑

○ ♓   FRIDAY 13

○ ♓ ♈ Full Moon 05:32   SATURDAY 14

○ ♈   SUNDAY 15

THIS WEEK

Take a look up in the sky at this week's Micromoon.
Does it seem smaller to you? It should do!

....

16 MONDAY   ♈︎○

....

17 TUESDAY   ♉︎○

....

18 WEDNESDAY   ♉︎○

....

19 THURSDAY   ♉︎♊︎○

....

◐ ♊   FRIDAY 20

◐ ♊   SATURDAY 21

◑ ♋   SUNDAY 22

THIS WEEK

*The beautiful goddess of compassion, Kuan Yin, directs
the sign of Pisces, so call on her this week if you need
to open your heart and forgive someone for something.*

New Moon in Libra

A chance to start over in your relationship(s).

London	28 September	19:26
Sydney	29 September	04:26
Los Angeles	28 September	11:26

What a week lies for ahead for relationships! We have the New Moon in the partnership sign of Libra, and the love planet, Venus, goes from a clash with nasty Saturn to a loving connection with Jupiter.

If your love life feels like it's lost its mind this week, then now you know why! Let's break it down...

Midweek brings the Venus-Saturn clash. This is always a key event, but extra important this week because of the New Moon in Libra (as Libra is the sign associated with the planet Venus). So don't be surprised if your relationships are feeling a little bit less than loving as the week begins. And if midweek it feels like someone just isn't there for you, if it feels like there isn't enough love (or for that matter, money) to go around, don't panic. Think good thoughts, do your practices (yoga, meditation, chanting and so on) and focus on the love in your heart. Ask the Libra Archangel

Jophiel, or the goddess of love, Aphrodite, for help. You can also talk to Lakshmi and Kuan Yin.

Later in the week is the Libra New Moon – always the time to make wishes about love, or to set your intentions for your love life in the year ahead. Then comes the sweet relief of a Venus connection to the planet of plenty, Jupiter.

This is a week to be conscious of *how* you are in relationships, and to think about what you want. As you fall asleep each night, visualize your ideal day with your beloved (whether he or she has manifested yet or not).

The Month Ahead

Here's where the New Moon is triggering your chart. See p.11 for a quick guide to the Houses and read your Rising sign if you know it: Aries – 7th House; Taurus – 6th House; Gemini – 5th House; Cancer – 4th House; Leo – 3rd House; Virgo – 2nd House; Libra – 1st House; Scorpio – 12th House; Sagittarius – 11th House; Capricorn – 10th House; Aquarius – 9th House; Pisces – 8th House.

Connect with the Goddess

The Hindu festival of Navratri begins on 29 September and lasts for nine nights. Followers pay homage to the Goddess Durga, who has the power to destroy ignorance and evil. She represents the energy of the Universe, and is envisioned in her nine beautiful forms during the festival.

Chant the mantra *Om Dum Durgayei Namaha* for the duration of the festival, and see how your world changes.

New Moon Wishes and Intentions

Decide on your top 10 wishes and/or intentions for the coming four weeks. Be as specific or as vague as you like. Also decide what you can commit to doing, in order to make your wishes come true. If you like, visit my website to access a worksheet on which you can write your wish lists. You'll also find an audio guide to support you in the process.

_____

_____

_____

_____

_____

_____

_____

_____

_____

_____

Questions to Ask at This New Moon

How can I improve my most important relationships?

_____

_____

_____

_____

Where am I giving or taking too much, and am I ready to redress the balance?

_____

_____

_____

_____

Can I put on some rose-coloured glasses and see the best in people?

_____

_____

_____

SEPTEMBER WEEK 39

··

23 MONDAY

··
Autumn Equinox/Mabon (UK); Spring Equinox/Ostara (Aus)
··

24 TUESDAY

··

25 WEDNESDAY

··

26 THURSDAY

··

⬤ ♍   FRIDAY 27

⬤ ♎ **New Moon 19:26**   SATURDAY 28

⬤ ♎   SUNDAY 29

THIS WEEK

*If you're looking for romance, Saturday night's New Moon
promises lovely possibilities! It's also a Supermoon, so be
doubly sure you make your wishes and set your intentions!*

SEPT/OCT WEEK 40

30 MONDAY ♏ ●

1 TUESDAY ♏♐ ◐

2 WEDNESDAY ♐ ◐

3 THURSDAY ♐ ◐

◐ ♐ ♑   FRIDAY 4

◐ ♑   SATURDAY 5

◐ ♑   SUNDAY 6

THIS WEEK

*With all the Libra energy right now, it's a
superb time to work on your relationships.*

Full Moon in Aries

A super-energetically charged Moon in fiery Aries!

London	13 October	22:07
Sydney	14 October	08:07
Los Angeles	13 October	14:07

The start of the week is going to be tougher than the second, when the Full Moon arrives to break the tension and herald some easier astrology.

In the first half of the week, the stand-out obstacle to peace, love and happiness is a clash between the Sun (ego) and Saturn (tedious taskmaster, strict headmaster and crone). So while you may wish to live your life, Saturn may have other ideas, which will be presented to you in the form of challenges, rules and limitations.

The Full Moon in Aries is actually a wonderful antidote to this negative energy (which peaks on Monday), as Aries is the child of the zodiac and perhaps the sign least willing to listen to what Saturn has to say. If you feel bossed about by someone, check to see if there is a lesson you need to learn. However, if you feel that they're being too demanding, wait for the Full Moon and the energy will dissipate.

The great news is that if love or money matters are weighing on your mind, there could be a total turnaround this week. Plus, the Full Moon is harmoniously aspecting the planet of good news and good times, Jupiter.

All in all, the outlook is positive. Be sure, even if you're feeling high on life, to take a moment at the Full Moon to connect with the Divine forces via chanting or prayer.

 ## The Month Ahead

Here's where the Full Moon is triggering your chart. See p.11 for a quick guide to the Houses and read your Rising sign if you know it: Aries – 1st House; Taurus – 12th House; Gemini – 11th House; Cancer – 10th House; Leo – 9th House; Virgo – 8th House; Libra – 7th House; Scorpio – 6th House; Sagittarius – 5th House; Capricorn – 4th House; Aquarius – 3rd House; Pisces – 2nd House.

 ## Practise Gratitude

If you feel too happy to do your monthly negativity release work, then focus on your gratitude practice instead:

1. Sit down somewhere quiet.

2. Breathe slowly and deeply, focusing on the rise and fall of your breath.

3. Bring to mind someone or something you're truly grateful for, and then hold that vision.

4. Say (silently or out loud), 'Thank you, Universe, thank you!', and then slowly open your eyes.

Full Moon Forgiveness List

Who do you need to forgive this month? Write out their name and then forgive them. They are more than likely doing their best, believe it or not!

_____

_____

_____

_____

_____

_____

_____

_____

_____

_____

_____

Questions to Ask at This Full Moon

Where do I need to slow down and be less impulsive?

_____

_____

_____

_____

Have I been acting like a child? How can I make sure I stop that?

_____

_____

_____

If I'm not having enough fun, how can I have more?

_____

_____

_____

_____

OCTOBER WEEK 41

7 MONDAY ≈◐

8 TUESDAY ≈◐

9 WEDNESDAY ≈)(◯

10 THURSDAY)(◯

☉ ♓   FRIDAY **11**

☉ ♈   SATURDAY **12**

☉ ♈ Full Moon 22:07   SUNDAY **13**

THIS WEEK

*As the Moon swells to fullness, Saturday is a
highly charged day as loving and abundant Venus
opposes mad Uranus. Anything could happen, and
probably will when it comes to love and money!*

OCTOBER Week 42

14 MONDAY ♈ ♉ ○

15 TUESDAY ♉ ○

16 WEDNESDAY ♉ ○

17 THURSDAY ♊ ○

FRIDAY **18**

SATURDAY **19**

SUNDAY **20**

THIS WEEK

*We're now in the waning cycle – a time to
exhale and release, exhale and release…*

OCTOBER WEEK 43

21 MONDAY ♋♌☽

22 TUESDAY ♌☽

23 WEDNESDAY ♌♍☽

24 THURSDAY ♍🌑

WEEK 43 OCTOBER

☽ ♍︎ ♎︎   FRIDAY 25

● ♎︎   SATURDAY 26

● ♎︎ ♏︎   SUNDAY 27

THIS WEEK

This is the ideal time to release toxic habits or people from your life...

New Moon in Scorpio

This is a week to pay attention!

London	28 October	03:38
Sydney	28 October	14:38
Los Angeles	27 October	20:38

This week brings a wild New Moon, powerful celebrations and Mercury going retrograde, so it's a time to pay attention.

It feels like life is hotting up energetically as we move towards the end of the year. This week brings the New Moon in the deep and mysterious sign of Scorpio. But wait, there's more! The New Moon is directly opposite the planet of change and madness, Uranus. So what can we expect?

Scorpio is the sign that likes to go deep, to plumb the depths and deal with superficiality. Uranus is the planet that governs chaos theory and unpredictability, and is also about awakenings and revolutions. So while we can make some wild guesses about what this New Moon will bring, there's also very much a feeling of 'wait and see'.

So look at where in your life you have been thinking deeply about something, and where you might have acted a tad shadily. These are the areas where this 'woke' New Moon can wake you up and help you to become unstuck, or could even bring you a surprise or a rude awakening!

If you've been feeling hemmed in, use this New Moon as a point of change. Pivot to face the direction in which you want to go. It's a week when change is very much on the agenda, so don't just sit around – do something!

It's actually quite rare to have such a powerful planet as Uranus triggered so directly by a lunation. There is no doubt that our New Moon wishes and intentions this month will have extra powers to create change.

 The Month Ahead

Here's where the New Moon will affect you. See p.11 for a quick guide to the Houses and read your Rising sign if you know it: Aries – 8th House; Taurus – 7th House; Gemini – 6th House; Cancer – 5th House; Leo – 4th House; Virgo – 3rd House; Libra – 2nd House; Scorpio – 1st House; Sagittarius – 12th House; Capricorn – 11th House; Aquarius – 10th House; Pisces – 9th House.

Intention is Everything

The added energy of the New Moon opposite changemaker Uranus makes this a week to celebrate new directions. So instead of waiting until the new year, harness the energy of change in the air this week and write down how you want your life to change, and what you're going to do to bring about that change. Intention really is everything!

New Moon Wishes and Intentions

Decide on your top 10 wishes and/or intentions for the coming four weeks. Be as specific or as vague as you like. Also decide what you can commit to doing, in order to make your wishes come true. If you like, visit my website to access a worksheet on which you can write your wish lists. You'll also find an audio guide to support you in the process.

_____

_____

_____

_____

_____

_____

_____

_____

_____

_____

Questions to Ask at This New Moon

How's my sex life and what can I do to make it (even) better?

_____

_____

_____

Who do you need to forgive? What would life be like if you released this grudge?

_____

_____

_____

What are the top five changes I want to see in my life?

_____

_____

_____

_____

_____

OCTOBER WEEK 44

· ·

28 MONDAY   New Moon 03.38 ♏

· ·

29 TUESDAY   ♏♐

· ·

30 WEDNESDAY   ♐ ●

· ·

31 THURSDAY   ♐ ●

Festivals of Samhain (UK) and Beltane (Aus)

· ·

WEEK 44 NOVEMBER

....

◑ ♐   FRIDAY 1

....

◑ ♐   SATURDAY 2

....

◑ ♒   SUNDAY 3

....

THIS WEEK

*This week brings the festival of Samhain (marking the
beginning of winter) in the northern hemisphere, and Beltane
(marking the beginning of summer) in the southern hemisphere.
Mercury starts a new retrograde cycle on 31 October.*

November Week 45

4 **Monday**   ≈≈ ◑

5 **Tuesday**   ≈≈ ⊬ ◐

6 **Wednesday**   ⊬ ◐

7 **Thursday**   ⊬ ◐

WEEK 45 NOVEMBER

O ♈

FRIDAY 8

O ♈

SATURDAY 9

O ♈ ♉

SUNDAY 10

THIS WEEK

*Expect this week to be emotionally intense as
we move towards next week's Full Moon.*

Full Moon in Taurus

**As the Full Moon triggers powerful
Pluto, it's time to release!**

London	12 November	13:34
Sydney	13 November	00:34
Los Angeles	12 November	05:34

Every Full Moon is a chance to release negativity. Some months and Full Moons are better than others when it comes to having the power to really purge, and this week's Full Moon is one of those. This is because it's taking place in harmonious aspect to the purge planet, Pluto.

Pluto is effectively the plumber of the zodiac. Think of when your drain is blocked and you use a plunger or baking soda and vinegar to clear the blockage. Pluto is the plunger or the dissolving solution. Note that the Full Moon is in harmonious aspect to Pluto, so this should be a gentle energy, rather than a jarring one. Chances like this really don't come along every week, so be sure to do the work. I've included an exercise (*see opposite*) to help you.

If you're still unclear about why releasing negativity is a good thing, the answer goes something like this: we're all creating our reality based on what we're 'putting out there' energetically. If you release negativity, such as upset, drama and jealousy, you're far less likely to radiate negativity and thus more likely to attract positivity.

Ideally, Full Moon releasing is something you should do every month. Think of it as an energetic clear-out. It's hard to over-emphasize how important this is.

☾ The Month Ahead

Here's where the Full Moon is triggering your chart. See p.11 for a quick guide to the Houses and read your Rising sign if you know it: Aries – 2nd House; Taurus – 1st House; Gemini – 12th House; Cancer – 11th House; Leo – 10th House; Virgo – 9th House; Libra – 8th House; Scorpio – 7th House; Sagittarius – 6th House; Capricorn – 5th House; Aquarius – 4th House; Pisces – 3rd House.

☾ The 'No More' Exercise

This is such a powerful week, so as well as your regular Full Moon forgiveness ceremony, add this meditation:

1. Write down on strips of paper any negativity you need to release. Have you been jealous, angry or insecure?

2. Pick up a strip, read it silently and then declare out loud: 'No more!' Repeat until you have read all strips.

3. Scrunch the paper into a small ball and put it in a ceramic or steel bowl, or other fireproof receptacle.

4. Burn all the paper to ashes and throw away.

Full Moon Forgiveness List

Who do you need to forgive this month? Write out their name and then forgive them. They are more than likely doing their best, believe it or not!

_____

_____

_____

_____

_____

_____

_____

_____

_____

_____

Questions to Ask at This Full Moon

Have I been obsessing about money or status symbols? If so, how can I stop?

_____

_____

_____

_____

Do I need to improve my diet and exercise more? What needs doing?

_____

_____

_____

Where I'm not forgiving someone, am I just being stubborn?

_____

_____

_____

NOVEMBER WEEK 46

. . . .

11 MONDAY   ♉ ◯

. . . .

12 TUESDAY   Full Moon 13:34 ♉ ◯

. . . .

13 WEDNESDAY   ♊ ◯

. . . .

14 THURSDAY   ♊ ◯

. . . .

New Moon in Sagittarius

A great week for meditation, love and abundance.

London	26 November	15:05
Sydney	27 November	02:05
Los Angeles	26 November	07:05

The week ahead looks inspired for anyone who is on the spiritual path, meditates, chants, is looking for love or has a good relationship with abundance.

The New Moon takes place in the sign of Sagittarius, the sign associated with study, travel, adventure, higher consciousness, life philosophies, learning and teaching.

Meanwhile the planets this New Moon week are very benevolent: a Mercury-Neptune link will aid anyone who is a meditator or chanter. If you already have a practice, then make sure you do it! Meditating and chanting are two of the simplest ways to connect to the Universe and the Divine. As my teacher Narayani Amma says, 'To connect with the Divine is the purpose of this life. We do it because it feels good, but also it's the purpose of being human!'

In more mundane matters, note that a lovely Venus-Uranus link this week augurs well for anyone hoping for

FRIDAY 22

SATURDAY 23

SUNDAY 24

THIS WEEK

This week's Quarter Moon activates lucky Jupiter so chant, 'I'm lucky!' to tap into the positive vibes. Mercury ends its retrograde cycle on 20 November in Scorpio.

NOVEMBER WEEK 47

....

18 MONDAY   ♌ ◑

....

19 TUESDAY   ♌ ◑

....

20 WEDNESDAY   ♍ ◑

....

21 THURSDAY   ♍ ◑

....

WEEK 46 NOVEMBER

○ ♊ ♋   FRIDAY 15

○ ♋   SATURDAY 16

○ ♋ ♌   SUNDAY 17

THIS WEEK

This week brings a Venus–Neptune clash just after
the Full Moon. This could translate as confusion
about love or money, so remember to focus on
solutions rather than problems if issues arise.

a turnaround regarding romance or riches. If you're not happy with the status quo when it comes to money or love, talk things through and you could get a very positive result. In addition, agreements made this New Moon week are likely to stick, thanks to a Mercury-Saturn connection which will also help to set your New Moon intentions in stone.

The Month Ahead

Here's where the New Moon is triggering your chart. See p.11 for a quick guide to the Houses and read your Rising sign if you know it: Aries – 9th House; Taurus – 8th House; Gemini – 7th House; Cancer – 6th House; Leo – 5th House; Virgo – 4th House; Libra – 3rd House; Scorpio – 2nd House; Sagittarius – 1st House; Capricorn – 12th House; Aquarius – 11th House; Pisces – 10th House.

An Invocation to Bring Luck

This is an invocation to the goddess of luck, Fortuna. Pour a glass of wine or juice, light a green candle and say these words:

> *Goddess Fortuna, blessed be!*
> *Bring your luck near to me!*
> *Be by my side while I need you most!*
> *Goddess Fortuna, to you I make this toast!*

Drink the drink and declare, 'I have the Goddess Fortuna on my side!'

New Moon Wishes and Intentions

Decide on your top 10 wishes and/or intentions for the coming four weeks. Be as specific or as vague as you like. Also decide what you can commit to doing, in order to make your wishes come true. If you like, visit my website to access a worksheet on which you can write your wish lists. You'll also find an audio guide to support you in the process.

_____

_____

_____

_____

_____

_____

_____

_____

_____

Questions to Ask at This New Moon

Do you feel lucky? Do you feel blessed? Make a list of where you know the Universe smiles on you.

_____

_____

_____

_____

Where do I need to find balance? Have I been taking too many risks or too few?

_____

_____

_____

_____

Travel broadens the mind – when can I next get away?

_____

_____

_____

NOVEMBER WEEK 48

....

25 MONDAY ♏ ●

....

26 TUESDAY New Moon 15:05 ♐ ●

....

27 WEDNESDAY ♐ ●

....

28 THURSDAY ♐ ♑ ●

....

FRIDAY 29

SATURDAY 30

SUNDAY 1

THIS WEEK

*This Friday – no matter where in the
world you are – is the ideal day to sign
a contract you want to make stick.*

DECEMBER WEEK 49

2 MONDAY ♒ ☽

3 TUESDAY ♓ ☽

4 WEDNESDAY ♓ ☽

5 THURSDAY ♓ ♈ ☽

☽♈   FRIDAY 6

☽♈   SATURDAY 7

☽♉   SUNDAY 8

THIS WEEK

The goddess of Sagittarius is Fortuna – Sagittarius is the lucky sign and Fortuna is the lucky goddess. Appeal to her if you need luck on your side this week (or ever!).

Full Moon in Gemini

Big changes are possible.

London	12 December	05:12
Sydney	12 December	16:12
Los Angeles	11 December	21:12

Against the backdrop of the Full Moon in Gemini, we get a connection between massive planets Jupiter and Uranus this week. It's a very promising start to the last month of the year.

The Full Moon always brings a kind of climax. Throughout the waxing cycle, the Moon grows rounder in the sky until She's a seemingly perfect sphere. Then we move into the much softer waning cycle, when the Moon gets smaller as She completes Her lunation. In the waxing cycle matters are rising up. So what is rising up in you as the week starts? In the waning cycle, things are falling away. What are you ready to release?

This week we also have a fantastic link between Jupiter and Uranus – Jupiter being the planet of plenty and Uranus being the planet of change and revolution. So where do you need a big revolution in your life?

One of the best ways to usher new things into your life is to create room for them. That means making space by clearing out the old and, obviously, the Full Moon is the ideal time to let things go. Let me say again, don't wait for the new year before you start to release: begin it now!

The Full Moon in Gemini is also a great time to empty your brain of thoughts and ideas that no longer serve you. Negative thoughts lead to negative deeds, which lead to negative karma! So let them go. Living consciously means working to rid your mind of fear and doubt. Commit to that this week.

The Month Ahead

Here's where the Full Moon is triggering your chart. See p.11 for a quick guide to the Houses and read your Rising sign if you know it: Aries – 3rd House; Taurus – 2nd House; Gemini – 1st House; Cancer – 12th House; Leo – 11th House; Virgo – 10th House; Libra – 9th House; Scorpio – 8th House; Sagittarius – 7th House; Capricorn – 6th House; Aquarius – 5th House; Pisces – 4th House.

Creating Luck

With the line-up of planets in hard-working Capricorn now, including lucky Jupiter, here's something to ponder. The father of Sir Andrew Lloyd Webber was once told by an interviewer: 'Your son is so lucky', to which Mr Lloyd Webber senior replied: 'Yes, the harder he works, the luckier he gets.' Think about it.

Full Moon Forgiveness List

Who do you need to forgive this month? Write out their name and then forgive them. They are more than likely doing their best, believe it or not!

_____

_____

_____

_____

_____

_____

_____

_____

_____

_____

Questions to Ask at This Full Moon

When have I been gossipy or superficial this month?

_____

_____

_____

Do I need to do some more flirting? If so, will I? Flirting makes the world go round!

_____

_____

_____

_____

Are there any areas where I should be more positive?

_____

_____

_____

_____

DECEMBER WEEK 50

9 MONDAY ♉○

10 TUESDAY ♉♊○

11 WEDNESDAY ♊○

12 THURSDAY Full Moon 05:12 ♊♋○

◯ ♋ FRIDAY **13**

◯ ♋ SATURDAY **14**

◯ ♌ SUNDAY **15**

THIS WEEK

*This is the last Full Moon of the year! Make
sure you do your Full Moon negativity release
work to cast off any darkness from 2019.*

December Week 51

16 Monday ♌ ◐

17 Tuesday ♍ ◑

18 Wednesday ♍ ◑

19 Thursday ♎ ◑

FRIDAY **20**

SATURDAY **21**

SUNDAY **22**

Winter Solstice/Yule (UK); Summer Solstice/Litha (Aus)

THIS WEEK

In the northern hemisphere, 22 December brings the Winter Solstice or midwinter – marking the day with the shortest period of daylight. In the southern hemisphere it's the Summer Solstice or midsummer – the longest day.

New Moon Eclipse in Capricorn

What are you creating?

London	26 December	05:12
Sydney	26 December	16:12
Los Angeles	25 December	21:12

Where Capricorn is for you now is where there is a lot of power. This isn't just because of the New Moon this week, but because mega-planets Jupiter, Saturn and Pluto are also there.

Remember that Capricorn is all about strategizing, making plans and commitments, and working out how you're going to build the life you dream of. We're all so busy at this time of the year, but wise people will harness this New Moon energy and work out some tactics for 2020. This is a time to be ambitious. Capricorn knows that hard work is the way to achieving your long-term goals.

The good news is that, as the year ends, the energy is still quite fluid, so keep on aiming for the changes you want to see in your life. Moreover, there is going to be a real sense of optimism in the air thanks to a great Sun-Jupiter meeting. So go into 2020 expecting the best – and you might just get it!

The Month Ahead

Here's where the New Moon is triggering your chart. See p.11 for a quick guide to the Houses and read your Rising sign if you know it: Aries – 10th House; Taurus – 9th House; Gemini – 8th House; Cancer – 7th House; Leo – 6th House; Virgo – 5th House; Libra – 4th House; Scorpio – 3rd House; Sagittarius – 2nd House; Capricorn – 1st House; Aquarius – 12th House; Pisces – 11th House.

Make a Gratitude List

As soon as possible after the New Moon, or on 31 December, take some time to make a goodbye or gratitude list:

1. Think about what went wrong this year. What upset you and what do you need to let go of? What or who do you plan *not* to take into 2020 with you?

2. Write it down and then, you guessed it, burn it and transmute it into the ethers.

3. Then make a list of all the people, places, things and adventures from 2019 that you're grateful for.

4. Think about how blessed you are, and if you haven't already, start to make your list of intentions for 2020.

As you know, planning and writing things down are the main secrets to manifesting!

New Moon Wishes and Intentions

This New Moon week it's oh-so important to do some work on yourself. We might be at the party end of the year when everyone is having fun, but if you're serious about living consciously then make a list of your plans and wishes for the year ahead – do it as soon after the New Moon as you can. Really think about it and go into detail. Doing this with a friend can make this an even more powerful process.

_____

_____

_____

_____

_____

_____

_____

_____

_____

_____

_____

Questions to Ask at This New Moon

What is my biggest ambition for 2020, work-wise?

_____

_____

What is my biggest ambition for 2020, personally?

_____

_____

Do I dare write a 12-month plan? Yes, I do (so please do it)!

_____

_____

_____

_____

_____

_____

_____

DECEMBER WEEK 52

....

23 MONDAY ♏︎⚲♐︎ ☽

....

24 TUESDAY ♐︎ ☽

....

25 WEDNESDAY ♐︎ ♑︎ ☽

....

26 THURSDAY New Moon Eclipse 05:12 ♑︎ ●

....

FRIDAY 27

SATURDAY 28

SUNDAY 29

THIS WEEK

As we move into 2020, we'll be in the waxing cycle of the Moon, the part of the lunar cycle where things are on the up. It's a lovely way to start the new year!

Dec/Jan 2020 Week 1

30 Monday ≋)(◐

31 Tuesday)(◐

1 Wednesday)(◐

2 Thursday ♈ ◑

Week 1 January 2020

◐ ♈   Friday 3

◐ ♈ ♉   Saturday 4

◐ ♉   Sunday 5

This Week

*Whatever else you do on New Year's Eve, take a moment
to thank the Universe for all the good in your life.*

Moonology Diary 2019

JANUARY

M	T	W	T	F	S	S
		1	2	3	4	5
6	7	8	9	10	11	12
13	14	15	16	17	18	19
20	21	22	23	24	25	26
27	28	29	30	31		

FEBRUARY

M	T	W	T	F	S	S
					1	2
3	4	5	6	7	8	9
10	11	12	13	14	15	16
17	18	19	20	21	22	23
24	25	26	27	28	29	

MARCH

M	T	W	T	F	S	S
						1
2	3	4	5	6	7	8
9	10	11	12	13	14	15
16	17	18	19	20	21	22
23	24	25	26	27	28	29
30	31					

APRIL

M	T	W	T	F	S	S
1	2	3	4	5		
6	7	8	9	10	11	12
13	14	15	16	17	18	19
20	21	22	23	24	25	26
27	28	29	30			

MAY

M	T	W	T	F	S	S
		1	2	3		
4	5	6	7	8	9	10
11	12	13	14	15	16	17
18	19	20	21	22	23	24
25	26	27	28	29	30	31

JUNE

M	T	W	T	F	S	S
1	2	3	4	5	6	7
8	9	10	11	12	13	14
15	16	17	18	19	20	21
22	23	24	25	26	27	28
29	30					

JULY

M	T	W	T	F	S	S
		1	2	3	4	5
6	7	8	9	10	11	12
13	14	15	16	17	18	19
20	21	22	23	24	25	26
27	28	29	30	31		

AUGUST

M	T	W	T	F	S	S
					1	2
3	4	5	6	7	8	9
10	11	12	13	14	15	16
17	18	19	20	21	22	23
24	25	26	27	28	29	30
31						

SEPTEMBER

M	T	W	T	F	S	S
	1	2	3	4	5	6
7	8	9	10	11	12	13
14	15	16	17	18	19	20
21	22	23	24	25	26	27
28	29	30				

OCTOBER

M	T	W	T	F	S	S
			1	2	3	4
5	6	7	8	9	10	11
12	13	14	15	16	17	18
19	20	21	22	23	24	25
26	27	28	29	30	31	

NOVEMBER

M	T	W	T	F	S	S
						1
2	3	4	5	6	7	8
9	10	11	12	13	14	15
16	17	18	19	20	21	22
23	24	25	26	27	28	29
30						

DECEMBER

M	T	W	T	F	S	S
	1	2	3	4	5	6
7	8	9	10	11	12	13
14	15	16	17	18	19	20
21	22	23	24	25	26	27
28	29	30	31			

Reminders

_____

_____

_____

_____

_____

_____

_____

_____

_____

_____

_____

_____

_____